DOING YOUR OWN BOOK-KEEPING

It is a legal requirement to keep business records for income tax purposes. This *Best Small Business Accounts Book* should be acceptable to the Inland Revenue for Self Assessment provided you keep accurate and complete records and they are backed up with the documents described below.

How To Use This *Best Small Business Accounts Book*
Starting at Week 1 (which is either your first week of trading or the first week of your tax year), you complete one page of this book per week. There are 53 identical pages to cover one trading year. Each page records all your business transactions in that week. It may help if you do your figures in pencil to begin with, and then ink them in later. A worked example and instructions follow this page.

At Your Year End By "year end" we are referring to your financial (tax) year rather than the calendar year. You need to complete the five "At Year End" and Annual Summary pages which appear after Week 53 in this book. They provide data for your Tax Return, so are important. To prepare your annual Tax Return, you would be well advised to use a qualified accountant.

Cashflow Forecasting Near the end of this book is a blank Cashflow Forecast. Although not required by the tax inspector or your accountant, using it should help you to manage your finances better, especially if you are buying or selling on credit.

VAT This book is not suitable for a VAT registered business.

Records You Should Keep
A Record of Payments (Purchases & Expenses) You need to keep the invoices for *everything* you spend in connection with your business as proof of that expenditure. An invoice should give the supplier's name and address, date, amount and a description of the purchase. Other than for small amounts, it should also give your business (trading) name and address.

Invoices should all be filed in some manner. Those paid by cheque should be filed in *cheque number* sequence and one suggestion is to use a 2-hole lever arch file, as shown below. Write the cheque number on an outside corner of the invoice so that it can be cross-referred to easily. Invoices too small to be hole-punched can first be stuck to a larger piece of plain paper.

You can use a card divider in the lever arch file to separate *paid* from *unpaid* invoices. Put unpaid invoices on the left side of the card, and when you pay them, move them to the other side of the card. This should help you keep things under control.

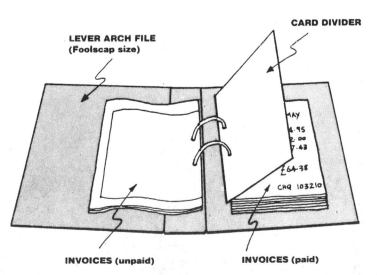

LEVER ARCH FILE
(Foolscap size)

CARD DIVIDER

INVOICES (unpaid)

INVOICES (paid)

The invoices (or receipts) for cash payments could be kept in an envelope (one for each week) or you could file them in another lever arch file. These invoices (or receipts) should be in *date sequence* and numbered sequentially from 001.

A Record of Sales (& Other Income) You need to keep a record of your sales. In a shop this could be the cash till roll, while in other businesses you should raise an invoice (each numbered sequentially) for each sale and keep a copy. You also need a record of any other income, eg National Lottery takings.

Additional Records You must also retain your business bank statements, pay-in books, cheque book stubs, orders and delivery notes, relevant business correspondence, import and export documents, copies of any credit/debit notes and a list of goods taken from the business for personal use or supplied to someone else in exchange for goods or services. In addition, if you transfer any money between your business and personal bank or building society accounts, then you must also retain those statements or pass books. You must also record all purchases/sales of assets used in your business (space is provided in the "At Year End" pages). Ask your accountant in advance what records they will want to see at the end of the year. (Note: If you employ any staff or make payments to subcontractors in the construction industry, you may need to keep further records).

Typical Book-Keeping Problems – and their Solutions
- [ ] If you use your private car or home phone partly for business use, you must keep a record of business usage. Pay these bills by business cheque, but at the end of your tax year you can only claim the business usage proportion as expenses.

- [ ] If unsure whether an invoice is a *business* expense, enter it in this book but add a query in pencil for your accountant.

- [ ] If you pay for business expenses with your credit card, when the card statement arrives, pay for those business items listed on the card statement using a business cheque.

- [ ] If you trade as a sole-trader or partnership and you transfer money into a personal account, then enter it as "Drawings".

- [ ] If you are in overdraft, this is normally shown in accounts by brackets, eg (210.35) means -£210.35.

- [ ] As you are not VAT registered, if an invoice includes VAT, then in this Accounts Book you must record the full invoice value, inclusive of any VAT you have been charged.

CAUTION The instructions in this book are for general guidance only and should not be regarded as a complete or authoritative statement of the law. You are strongly advised to consult an accountant, the Inland Revenue and, where necessary, HM Customs & Excise (for VAT).

Copyright © 1998 by Peter Hingston. All rights reserved worldwide. No copying permitted. Previous version: Copyright © 1991.
Published by Hingston Publishing Co., Honeymoor Lodge, Eaton Bishop, Hereford HR2 9QT. Tel: 01981 251621.
Printed and bound in Great Britain by The Bath Press, Bath · 14th Printing (January 2003)   ISBN 0 906555 11 6

Week
commencing ... **2nd February** ...

MONEY RECORD

Money in hand at start of week	£	p
	178	23

DAILY TAKINGS

	£	p
Monday	63	12
Tuesday	39	73
Wednesday	127	32
Thursday	98	40
Friday	122	43
Saturday	163	82
Sunday		
Total Takings	**614**	**82**

OTHER MONEY, LOANS etc

	£	p
From Private a/c	1000	00
.		
.		
Cash from Bank	80	00
Total	1080	00

WEEK'S MONEY BALANCE

	£	p
£ at start of week	178	23
+ Daily Takings	614	82
+ Other Money	1080	00
– Daily Bankings	1571	71
– Cash Payments	191	02
Leaves: **Balance**	**110**	**32**

↓ Carry these figures forward to next week ↑

Money in hand at end of week		
	110	22

Discrepancy ±	–	10p

© P. Hingston

BANK RECORD

Bank Balance at start of week	£	p
	841	27

DAILY BANKINGS

	£	p
Monday	158	23
Tuesday		
Wednesday	80	65
Thursday		
Friday	1332	83
Saturday		
Sunday		
Total Bankings	**1571**	**71**

BANK DIRECT CREDITS/DEBITS

	£	p
Credits: **Grant**	500	00
Total Credits:	**500**	**00**
Debits:		
Interest	34	75
Finance Charges		
Cashed Cheques	80	00
Total Debits:	**114**	**75**

WEEK'S BANK BALANCE

	£	p
£ at start of week	841	27
+ Daily Bankings	1571	71
+ Direct Credits	500	00
– Direct Debits	114	75
– Chq. Payments	1954	16
Leaves: **Balance**	**844**	**07**

BANK STATEMENT CHECK

	£	p
Statement Balance	1011	24
Add any bankings	1332	83
Less any cheques (Not yet on Statement)	1500	00
Leaves: **Balance**	**844**	**07**

PAYMENTS RECORD

		Ref	BY CASH £	p	BY CHEQUE £	p
Stock/Raw Materials	**A. Jones**	133	22	20		
	A. Supply Co	072			87	23
	I.M. Quick	134	12	32		
	Brown & Son	073			107	24
	J. Smith Ltd	076			156	90
Stock/Raw Materials Sub-Totals			**34**	**52**	**351**	**37**
Employee Costs	Staff Wages					
	B. Good (Pt-time)	075			60	00
	A. Helper (Pt-time)	139	50	00		
	Staff PAYE/NIC					
Premises Costs	Business Rent					
	Business Rates					
	Cleaning					
	Electric/Gas/Heat/Water	074			23	79
	Property Insurance					
Repairs	Repairs/Maintenance					
General Admin. Expenses	Business Insurances					
	Postage/Parcels	136	1	12		
	Stationery/Printing	137	3	50		
	Subscriptions					
	Sundries	135 138	1	88		
	Telephone/Fax					
Motor Expenses	Fuel	078			19	00
	Repairs/Service					
	Tax/Insurance					
Travel & Subsistence						
Advertising & Promotion						
Legal & Professional	Fees (eg Solicitor or Accountant)					
Other Expenses						
Drawings/NIC	**Self**	140	100	00		
CAPITAL EXPENDITURE						
Van (2nd hand)		077			1500	00
Total Cash & Cheque Payments			**191**	**02**	**1954**	**16**

Week

commencing ....

PAYMENTS RECORD

INSTRUCTIONS for completing each Weekly page

	BY CASH		BY CHEQUE	
	£	p	£	p

This column is for your week's transactions in cash, cheques, POs and credit cards.

This column is for your week's business bank account transactions.

This column is for your week's payments by cash or cheque.

MONEY RECORD

Money in hand at start of week	£	p

This "start of week" figure is 0 if it is your first trading week. Otherwise it is the previous week's "end of week" figure.

DAILY TAKINGS

Monday		
Tuesday		
Wednesday		
Thursday		
Friday		
Saturday		
Sunday		
Total Takings		

Here you write your daily sales (including cash, cheques, POs and credit cards). If you sell something but are not paid until a later date, you show that sale only when you get paid.

OTHER MONEY, LOANS etc

Here you list any money which is not from sales, eg cash drawn from your business bank account, a loan, an asset sale, grant cheque, tax refund or money you put into the business. Always specify the source of the funds.

The amount shown here under "Cash from Bank" should equal "Cashed Cheques" (see right).

Cash from Bank		
Total		

WEEK'S MONEY BALANCE

£ at start of week		
+ Daily Takings		
+ Other Money		
− Daily Bankings		
− Cash Payments		
Leaves: **Balance**		

"Money in hand..." is the cash, cheques, POs and credit card vouchers as counted at the end of the week and is the amount carried forward to the next week.

The "Discrepancy" is the difference between the Balance and the money as counted.

© P. Hingston

BANK RECORD

Bank Balance at start of week	£	p

This "start of week" figure is 0 if it is your first trading week. Otherwise it is the previous week's Bank Balance figure.

DAILY BANKINGS

Monday		
Tuesday		
Wednesday		
Thursday		
Friday		
Saturday		
Sunday		
Total Bankings		

In the example opposite, the £1000 put into the business from the proprietor's private account is banked on the Friday together with £332.83 takings.

BANK DIRECT CREDITS

Direct Credits (eg a grant paid direct into your bank account) will appear on your Bank Statement as will Direct Debits (eg Bank Charges, Interest on overdrafts and most HP, Lease or Loan repayments).

Credits		
Total Credits.		

Known Direct Debits can be entered here on the appropriate dates, and new Debits/Credits can be added, for simplicity, on the week when your Statement arrives.

Debits		
Interest		
Finance Charges		
Cashed Cheques		
Total Debits:		

"Interest" is interest you pay on bank or other loans (or overdraft). "Finance Charges" are for any bank or credit card charges, HP interest or lease payments.

WEEK'S BANK BALANCE

When you get a Bank Statement, compare its Balance with that here. It may differ due to cheques you've written or pay-ins that haven't appeared yet on the Bank Statement.

£ at start of week		
+		
+ Direct Credits		
− Direct Debits		
Leaves: Balance		

The Week's Bank Balance becomes the Bank Balance at the start of the next Week.

BANK STATEMENT CHECK

Although this BANK STATEMENT CHECK appears on every Weekly page, you only need to complete it when you receive a Bank Statement.

Statement		
Add any bankings		
Less any cheques		
Leaves:		

The bottom line should equal the Week's Bank Balance above.

In the example opposite, Chq No. 077 and the Friday banking were not on the Bank Statement.

Payments Record (right side)

As a reference for a payment by cheque, use the last 3 figures of the cheque number.

As a reference for a cash payment, you could file cash invoices by payment date and insert that date here. Or you could give each invoice a number and use that number here instead.

If you need more lines, you can divide a space in two as shown below.

Stock/Raw Materials Sub-Totals				

The headings below left are those used in the Self Assessment Tax Return.

Employee Costs — of Wages

"Employee Costs" is where you record employees wages (also Directors salaries). Ideally, use a separate line for each person. (Note: NIC is National Insurance Contributions).

Staff PAYE/NIC				

Premises Costs
- Business Rent
- Business Rates
- Cleaning
- Electric/Gas/Heat/Water
- Property Insurance

Payments by Cash are paid either from your Daily Takings, or by drawing cash from your business bank account.

Repairs — Repairs/Maintenance

General Admin. Expenses
- Business Insurances
- Postage/Parcels
- Stationery/Printing
- Subscriptions
- Sundries
- Telephone

Where there is more than one transaction in a category in the week, then simply do a total in the appropriate cash or cheque column, and show the References.

Motor Expenses
- Fuel
- Repairs/Service
- Tax/Insurance

Travel & Subsistence

Advertising & Promotion

Note: only expenditure that is wholly and exclusively for your business is normally tax deductible.

Legal & Professional — Fees (eg Solicitor or Accountant)

Other Expenses

Drawings/NIC

This is for your own "wages" as a sole trader/partner (called "Drawings"), but if you are a company Director, record your salary under "Employee Costs" above.

CAPITAL EXPENDITURE

"Capital Expenditure" is eg vehicles, machinery, tools, office equipment, buildings etc.

Total Cash & Cheque Payments				

This total is entered in the WEEK'S MONEY BALANCE.

This total is entered in the WEEK'S BANK BALANCE.

Week 1
commencing ....

MONEY RECORD

	£	p
Money in hand at start of week		
DAILY TAKINGS		
Monday		
Tuesday		
Wednesday		
Thursday		
Friday		
Saturday		
Sunday		
Total Takings		
OTHER MONEY, LOANS etc		
Cash from Bank		
Total		
WEEK'S MONEY BALANCE		
£ at start of week		
+ Daily Takings		
+ Other Money		
– Daily Bankings		
– Cash Payments		
Leaves: **Balance**		
Money in hand at end of week		
Discrepancy ±		

© P. Hingston

BANK RECORD

	£	p
Bank Balance at start of week		
DAILY BANKINGS		
Monday		
Tuesday		
Wednesday		
Thursday		
Friday		
Saturday		
Sunday		
Total Bankings		
BANK DIRECT CREDITS/DEBITS		
Credits:		
Total Credits:		
Debits:		
Interest		
Finance Charges		
Cashed Cheques		
Total Debits:		
WEEK'S BANK BALANCE		
£ at start of week		
+ Daily Bankings		
+ Direct Credits		
– Direct Debits		
– Chq. Payments		
Leaves: **Balance**		

BANK STATEMENT CHECK

Statement Balance		
Add any bankings		
Less any cheques (Not yet on Statement)		
Leaves: **Balance**		

PAYMENTS RECORD

	Ref	BY CASH £	p	BY CHEQUE £	p
Stock/Raw Materials					
Stock/Raw Materials Sub-Totals					
Employee Costs — Staff Wages					
Employee Costs — Staff PAYE/NIC					
Premises Costs — Business Rent					
Premises Costs — Business Rates					
Premises Costs — Cleaning					
Premises Costs — Electric/Gas/Heat/Water					
Premises Costs — Property Insurance					
Repairs — Repairs/Maintenance					
General Admin. Expenses — Business Insurances					
General Admin. Expenses — Postage/Parcels					
General Admin. Expenses — Stationery/Printing					
General Admin. Expenses — Subscriptions					
General Admin. Expenses — Sundries					
General Admin. Expenses — Telephone/Fax					
Motor Expenses — Fuel					
Motor Expenses — Repairs/Service					
Motor Expenses — Tax/Insurance					
Travel & Subsistence					
Advertising & Promotion					
Legal & Professional — Fees (eg Solicitor or Accountant)					
Other Expenses					
Drawings/NIC					
CAPITAL EXPENDITURE					
Total Cash & Cheque Payments					

Week 2

commencing ....

MONEY RECORD

Money in hand at start of week	£	p

DAILY TAKINGS		
Monday		
Tuesday		
Wednesday		
Thursday		
Friday		
Saturday		
Sunday		
Total Takings		

OTHER MONEY, LOANS etc		
Cash from Bank		
Total		

WEEK'S MONEY BALANCE		
£ at start of week		
+ Daily Takings		
+ Other Money		
− Daily Bankings		
− Cash Payments		
Leaves: Balance		

Money in hand at end of week		

Discrepancy ±		

© P. Hingston

BANK RECORD

Bank Balance at start of week	£	p

DAILY BANKINGS		
Monday		
Tuesday		
Wednesday		
Thursday		
Friday		
Saturday		
Sunday		
Total Bankings		

BANK DIRECT CREDITS/DEBITS		
Credits:		
Total Credits:		
Debits:		
Interest		
Finance Charges		
Cashed Cheques		
Total Debits:		

WEEK'S BANK BALANCE		
£ at start of week		
+ Daily Bankings		
+ Direct Credits		
− Direct Debits		
− Chq. Payments		
Leaves: Balance		

BANK STATEMENT CHECK		
Statement Balance		
Add any bankings Less any cheques (Not yet on Statement)		
Leaves: Balance		

PAYMENTS RECORD

	Ref	BY CASH £	p	BY CHEQUE £	p
Stock/Raw Materials					
Stock/Raw Materials Sub-Totals					
Employee Costs — Staff Wages					
Staff PAYE/NIC					
Premises Costs — Business Rent					
Business Rates					
Cleaning					
Electric/Gas/Heat/Water					
Property Insurance					
Repairs — Repairs/Maintenance					
General Admin. Expenses — Business Insurances					
Postage/Parcels					
Stationery/Printing					
Subscriptions					
Sundries					
Telephone/Fax					
Motor Expenses — Fuel					
Repairs/Service					
Tax/Insurance					
Travel & Subsistence					
Advertising & Promotion					
Legal & Professional — Fees (eg Solicitor or Accountant)					
Other Expenses					
Drawings/NIC					
CAPITAL EXPENDITURE					
Total Cash & Cheque Payments					

Week 3

commencing . . . .

PAYMENTS RECORD

	Ref	BY CASH £	p	BY CHEQUE £	p
Stock/Raw Materials					
Stock/Raw Materials Sub-Totals					
Employee Costs — Staff Wages					
Employee Costs —					
Employee Costs — Staff PAYE/NIC					
Premises Costs — Business Rent					
Premises Costs — Business Rates					
Premises Costs — Cleaning					
Premises Costs — Electric/Gas/Heat/Water					
Premises Costs — Property Insurance					
Repairs — Repairs/Maintenance					
General Admin. Expenses — Business Insurances					
General Admin. Expenses — Postage/Parcels					
General Admin. Expenses — Stationery/Printing					
General Admin. Expenses — Subscriptions					
General Admin. Expenses — Sundries					
General Admin. Expenses — Telephone/Fax					
Motor Expenses — Fuel					
Motor Expenses — Repairs/Service					
Motor Expenses — Tax/Insurance					
Travel & Subsistence					
Advertising & Promotion					
Legal & Professional — Fees (eg Solicitor or Accountant)					
Other Expenses					
Drawings/NIC					
CAPITAL EXPENDITURE					
Total Cash & Cheque Payments					

MONEY RECORD

Money in hand at start of week	£	p

DAILY TAKINGS		
Monday		
Tuesday		
Wednesday		
Thursday		
Friday		
Saturday		
Sunday		
Total Takings		

OTHER MONEY, LOANS etc		
Cash from Bank		
Total		

WEEK'S MONEY BALANCE		
£ at start of week		
+ Daily Takings		
+ Other Money		
− Daily Bankings		
− Cash Payments		
Leaves: Balance		

Money in hand at end of week		

Discrepancy ±		

© P. Hingston

BANK RECORD

Bank Balance at start of week	£	p

DAILY BANKINGS		
Monday		
Tuesday		
Wednesday		
Thursday		
Friday		
Saturday		
Sunday		
Total Bankings		

BANK DIRECT CREDITS/DEBITS		
Credits:		
Total Credits:		
Debits:		
Interest		
Finance Charges		
Cashed Cheques		
Total Debits:		

WEEK'S BANK BALANCE		
£ at start of week		
+ Daily Bankings		
+ Direct Credits		
− Direct Debits		
− Chq. Payments		
Leaves: Balance		

BANK STATEMENT CHECK		
Statement Balance		
Add any bankings		
Less any cheques (Not yet on Statement)		
Leaves: Balance		

Week 4

commencing ....

MONEY RECORD

Money in hand at start of week	£	p
DAILY TAKINGS		
Monday		
Tuesday		
Wednesday		
Thursday		
Friday		
Saturday		
Sunday		
Total Takings		

OTHER MONEY, LOANS etc		
Cash from Bank		
Total		

WEEK'S MONEY BALANCE		
£ at start of week		
+ Daily Takings		
+ Other Money		
− Daily Bankings		
− Cash Payments		
Leaves: **Balance**		
Money in hand at end of week		
Discrepancy ±		

© P. Hingston

BANK RECORD

Bank Balance at start of week	£	p
DAILY BANKINGS		
Monday		
Tuesday		
Wednesday		
Thursday		
Friday		
Saturday		
Sunday		
Total Bankings		

BANK DIRECT CREDITS/DEBITS		
Credits:		
Total Credits:		
Debits:		
Interest		
Finance Charges		
Cashed Cheques		
Total Debits:		

WEEK'S BANK BALANCE		
£ at start of week		
+ Daily Bankings		
+ Direct Credits		
− Direct Debits		
− Chq. Payments		
Leaves: **Balance**		

BANK STATEMENT CHECK		
Statement Balance		
Add any bankings		
Less any cheques (Not yet on Statement)		
Leaves: **Balance**		

PAYMENTS RECORD

	Ref	BY CASH £	p	BY CHEQUE £	p
Stock/Raw Materials					
Stock/Raw Materials Sub-Totals					
Employee Costs	Staff Wages				
	Staff PAYE/NIC				
Premises Costs	Business Rent				
	Business Rates				
	Cleaning				
	Electric/Gas/Heat/Water				
	Property Insurance				
Repairs	Repairs/Maintenance				
General Admin. Expenses	Business Insurances				
	Postage/Parcels				
	Stationery/Printing				
	Subscriptions				
	Sundries				
	Telephone/Fax				
Motor Expenses	Fuel				
	Repairs/Service				
	Tax/Insurance				
Travel & Subsistence					
Advertising & Promotion					
Legal & Professional	Fees (eg Solicitor or Accountant)				
Other Expenses					
Drawings/NIC					
CAPITAL EXPENDITURE					
Total Cash & Cheque Payments					

Week 5

commencing . . . .

MONEY RECORD

Money in hand at start of week	£	p

DAILY TAKINGS		
Monday		
Tuesday		
Wednesday		
Thursday		
Friday		
Saturday		
Sunday		
Total Takings		

OTHER MONEY, LOANS etc		
Cash from Bank		
Total		

WEEK'S MONEY BALANCE		
£ at start of week		
+ Daily Takings		
+ Other Money		
− Daily Bankings		
− Cash Payments		
Leaves: **Balance**		

Money in hand at end of week		

Discrepancy ±		

© P. Hingston

BANK RECORD

Bank Balance at start of week	£	p

DAILY BANKINGS		
Monday		
Tuesday		
Wednesday		
Thursday		
Friday		
Saturday		
Sunday		
Total Bankings		

BANK DIRECT CREDITS/DEBITS		
Credits:		
Total Credits:		
Debits:		
Interest		
Finance Charges		
Cashed Cheques		
Total Debits:		

WEEK'S BANK BALANCE		
£ at start of week		
+ Daily Bankings		
+ Direct Credits		
− Direct Debits		
− Chq. Payments		
Leaves: **Balance**		

BANK STATEMENT CHECK		
Statement Balance		
Add any bankings		
Less any cheques (Not yet on Statement)		
Leaves: **Balance**		

PAYMENTS RECORD

	Ref	BY CASH £	p	BY CHEQUE £	p
Stock/Raw Materials					
Stock/Raw Materials Sub-Totals					
Employee Costs — Staff Wages					
Staff PAYE/NIC					
Premises Costs — Business Rent					
Business Rates					
Cleaning					
Electric/Gas/Heat/Water					
Property Insurance					
Repairs — Repairs/Maintenance					
General Admin. Expenses — Business Insurances					
Postage/Parcels					
Stationery/Printing					
Subscriptions					
Sundries					
Telephone/Fax					
Motor Expenses — Fuel					
Repairs/Service					
Tax/Insurance					
Travel & Subsistence					
Advertising & Promotion					
Legal & Professional — Fees (eg Solicitor or Accountant)					
Other Expenses					
Drawings/NIC					
CAPITAL EXPENDITURE					
Total Cash & Cheque Payments					

Week 6
commencing. . . . .

MONEY RECORD

	£	p
Money in hand at start of week		

DAILY TAKINGS		
Monday		
Tuesday		
Wednesday		
Thursday		
Friday		
Saturday		
Sunday		
Total Takings		

OTHER MONEY, LOANS etc		
Cash from Bank		
Total		

WEEK'S MONEY BALANCE		
£ at start of week		
+ Daily Takings		
+ Other Money		
− Daily Bankings		
− Cash Payments		
Leaves: Balance		

Money in hand at end of week		

Discrepancy ±		

© P. Hingston

BANK RECORD

	£	p
Bank Balance at start of week		

DAILY BANKINGS		
Monday		
Tuesday		
Wednesday		
Thursday		
Friday		
Saturday		
Sunday		
Total Bankings		

BANK DIRECT CREDITS/DEBITS		
Credits:		
Total Credits:		
Debits:		
Interest		
Finance Charges		
Cashed Cheques		
Total Debits:		

WEEK'S BANK BALANCE		
£ at start of week		
+ Daily Bankings		
+ Direct Credits		
− Direct Debits		
− Chq. Payments		
Leaves: Balance		

BANK STATEMENT CHECK		
Statement Balance		
Add any bankings		
Less any cheques (Not yet on Statement)		
Leaves: Balance		

PAYMENTS RECORD

		Ref	BY CASH £	p	BY CHEQUE £	p
Stock/Raw Materials						
Stock/Raw Materials Sub-Totals						
Employee Costs	Staff Wages					
	Staff PAYE/NIC					
Premises Costs	Business Rent					
	Business Rates					
	Cleaning					
	Electric/Gas/Heat/Water					
	Property Insurance					
Repairs	Repairs/Maintenance					
General Admin. Expenses	Business Insurances					
	Postage/Parcels					
	Stationery/Printing					
	Subscriptions					
	Sundries					
	Telephone/Fax					
Motor Expenses	Fuel					
	Repairs/Service					
	Tax/Insurance					
Travel & Subsistence						
Advertising & Promotion						
Legal & Professional	Fees (eg Solicitor or Accountant)					
Other Expenses						
Drawings/NIC						
CAPITAL EXPENDITURE						
Total Cash & Cheque Payments						

Week 7

commencing . . . .

MONEY RECORD

Money in hand at start of week	£	p

DAILY TAKINGS

Monday		
Tuesday		
Wednesday		
Thursday		
Friday		
Saturday		
Sunday		
Total Takings		

OTHER MONEY, LOANS etc

Cash from Bank		
Total		

WEEK'S MONEY BALANCE

£ at start of week		
+ Daily Takings		
+ Other Money		
− Daily Bankings		
− Cash Payments		
Leaves: **Balance**		
Money in hand at end of week		
Discrepancy ±		

© P. Hingston

BANK RECORD

Bank Balance at start of week	£	p

DAILY BANKINGS

Monday		
Tuesday		
Wednesday		
Thursday		
Friday		
Saturday		
Sunday		
Total Bankings		

BANK DIRECT CREDITS/DEBITS

Credits:		
Total Credits:		
Debits:		
Interest		
Finance Charges		
Cashed Cheques		
Total Debits:		

WEEK'S BANK BALANCE

£ at start of week		
+ Daily Bankings		
+ Direct Credits		
− Direct Debits		
− Chq. Payments		
Leaves: **Balance**		

BANK STATEMENT CHECK

Statement Balance		
Add any bankings		
Less any cheques (Not yet on Statement)		
Leaves: **Balance**		

PAYMENTS RECORD

	Ref	BY CASH £	p	BY CHEQUE £	p
Stock/Raw Materials					
Stock/Raw Materials Sub-Totals					
Employee Costs — Staff Wages					
Staff PAYE/NIC					
Premises Costs — Business Rent					
Business Rates					
Cleaning					
Electric/Gas/Heat/Water					
Property Insurance					
Repairs — Repairs/Maintenance					
General Admin. Expenses — Business Insurances					
Postage/Parcels					
Stationery/Printing					
Subscriptions					
Sundries					
Telephone/Fax					
Motor Expenses — Fuel					
Repairs/Service					
Tax/Insurance					
Travel & Subsistence					
Advertising & Promotion					
Legal & Professional — Fees (eg Solicitor or Accountant)					
Other Expenses					
Drawings/NIC					
CAPITAL EXPENDITURE					
Total Cash & Cheque Payments					

Week 8

commencing . . . .

MONEY RECORD

Money in hand at start of week	£	p

DAILY TAKINGS		
Monday		
Tuesday		
Wednesday		
Thursday		
Friday		
Saturday		
Sunday		
Total Takings		

OTHER MONEY, LOANS etc		
Cash from Bank		
Total		

WEEK'S MONEY BALANCE		
£ at start of week		
+ Daily Takings		
+ Other Money		
− Daily Bankings		
− Cash Payments		
Leaves: Balance		

Money in hand at end of week		

Discrepancy ±		

© P. Hingston

BANK RECORD

Bank Balance at start of week	£	p

DAILY BANKINGS		
Monday		
Tuesday		
Wednesday		
Thursday		
Friday		
Saturday		
Sunday		
Total Bankings		

BANK DIRECT CREDITS/DEBITS		
Credits:		
Total Credits:		
Debits:		
Interest		
Finance Charges		
Cashed Cheques		
Total Debits:		

WEEK'S BANK BALANCE		
£ at start of week		
+ Daily Bankings		
+ Direct Credits		
− Direct Debits		
− Chq. Payments		
Leaves: Balance		

BANK STATEMENT CHECK		
Statement Balance		
Add any bankings		
Less any cheques (Not yet on Statement)		
Leaves: Balance		

PAYMENTS RECORD

	Ref	BY CASH £	p	BY CHEQUE £	p
Stock/Raw Materials					
Stock/Raw Materials Sub-Totals					
Employee Costs	Staff Wages				
	Staff PAYE/NIC				
Premises Costs	Business Rent				
	Business Rates				
	Cleaning				
	Electric/Gas/Heat/Water				
	Property Insurance				
Repairs	Repairs/Maintenance				
General Admin. Expenses	Business Insurances				
	Postage/Parcels				
	Stationery/Printing				
	Subscriptions				
	Sundries				
	Telephone/Fax				
Motor Expenses	Fuel				
	Repairs/Service				
	Tax/Insurance				
Travel & Subsistence					
Advertising & Promotion					
Legal & Professional	Fees (eg Solicitor or Accountant)				
Other Expenses					
Drawings/NIC					
CAPITAL EXPENDITURE					
Total Cash & Cheque Payments					

Week 9

commencing.............................

MONEY RECORD

Money in hand at start of week	£	p

DAILY TAKINGS		
Monday		
Tuesday		
Wednesday		
Thursday		
Friday		
Saturday		
Sunday		
Total Takings		

OTHER MONEY, LOANS etc		
Cash from Bank		
Total		

WEEK'S MONEY BALANCE		
£ at start of week		
+ Daily Takings		
+ Other Money		
− Daily Bankings		
− Cash Payments		
Leaves: Balance		

Money in hand at end of week		

Discrepancy ±		

© P. Hingston

BANK RECORD

Bank Balance at start of week	£	p

DAILY BANKINGS		
Monday		
Tuesday		
Wednesday		
Thursday		
Friday		
Saturday		
Sunday		
Total Bankings		

BANK DIRECT CREDITS/DEBITS		
Credits:		
Total Credits:		
Debits:		
Interest		
Finance Charges		
Cashed Cheques		
Total Debits:		

WEEK'S BANK BALANCE		
£ at start of week		
+ Daily Bankings		
+ Direct Credits		
− Direct Debits		
− Chq. Payments		
Leaves: Balance		

BANK STATEMENT CHECK		
Statement Balance		
Add any bankings		
Less any cheques (Not yet on Statement)		
Leaves: Balance		

PAYMENTS RECORD

	Ref	BY CASH £	p	BY CHEQUE £	p
Stock/Raw Materials					
Stock/Raw Materials Sub-Totals					
Employee Costs — Staff Wages					
Employee Costs —					
Employee Costs — Staff PAYE/NIC					
Premises Costs — Business Rent					
Premises Costs — Business Rates					
Premises Costs — Cleaning					
Premises Costs — Electric/Gas/Heat/Water					
Premises Costs — Property Insurance					
Repairs — Repairs/Maintenance					
General Admin. Expenses — Business Insurances					
General Admin. Expenses — Postage/Parcels					
General Admin. Expenses — Stationery/Printing					
General Admin. Expenses — Subscriptions					
General Admin. Expenses — Sundries					
General Admin. Expenses — Telephone/Fax					
Motor Expenses — Fuel					
Motor Expenses — Repairs/Service					
Motor Expenses — Tax/Insurance					
Travel & Subsistence					
Advertising & Promotion					
Legal & Professional — Fees (eg Solicitor or Accountant)					
Other Expenses					
Drawings/NIC					
CAPITAL EXPENDITURE					
Total Cash & Cheque Payments					

Week 10

commencing.............................

MONEY RECORD

Money in hand at start of week	£	p

DAILY TAKINGS
Monday		
Tuesday		
Wednesday		
Thursday		
Friday		
Saturday		
Sunday		
Total Takings		

OTHER MONEY, LOANS etc
Cash from Bank		
Total		

WEEK'S MONEY BALANCE
£ at start of week		
+ Daily Takings		
+ Other Money		
− Daily Bankings		
− Cash Payments		
Leaves: **Balance**		

Money in hand at end of week		

Discrepancy ±		

© P. Hingston

BANK RECORD

Bank Balance at start of week	£	p

DAILY BANKINGS
Monday		
Tuesday		
Wednesday		
Thursday		
Friday		
Saturday		
Sunday		
Total Bankings		

BANK DIRECT CREDITS/DEBITS
Credits:		
Total Credits:		
Debits:		
Interest		
Finance Charges		
Cashed Cheques		
Total Debits:		

WEEK'S BANK BALANCE
£ at start of week		
+ Daily Bankings		
+ Direct Credits		
− Direct Debits		
− Chq. Payments		
Leaves: **Balance**		

BANK STATEMENT CHECK
Statement Balance		
Add any bankings		
Less any cheques (Not yet on Statement)		
Leaves: **Balance**		

PAYMENTS RECORD

	Ref	BY CASH £	p	BY CHEQUE £	p
Stock/Raw Materials					
Stock/Raw Materials Sub-Totals					
Employee Costs	Staff Wages				
	Staff PAYE/NIC				
Premises Costs	Business Rent				
	Business Rates				
	Cleaning				
	Electric/Gas/Heat/Water				
	Property Insurance				
Repairs	Repairs/Maintenance				
General Admin. Expenses	Business Insurances				
	Postage/Parcels				
	Stationery/Printing				
	Subscriptions				
	Sundries				
	Telephone/Fax				
Motor Expenses	Fuel				
	Repairs/Service				
	Tax/Insurance				
Travel & Subsistence					
Advertising & Promotion					
Legal & Professional	Fees (eg Solicitor or Accountant)				
Other Expenses					
Drawings/NIC					
CAPITAL EXPENDITURE					
Total Cash & Cheque Payments					

Week 11

commencing ....

MONEY RECORD

Money in hand at start of week	£	p

DAILY TAKINGS

Monday		
Tuesday		
Wednesday		
Thursday		
Friday		
Saturday		
Sunday		
Total Takings		

OTHER MONEY, LOANS etc

Cash from Bank		
Total		

WEEK'S MONEY BALANCE

£ at start of week		
+ Daily Takings		
+ Other Money		
− Daily Bankings		
− Cash Payments		
Leaves: **Balance**		

Money in hand at end of week		

Discrepancy ±		

© P. Hingston

BANK RECORD

Bank Balance at start of week	£	p

DAILY BANKINGS

Monday		
Tuesday		
Wednesday		
Thursday		
Friday		
Saturday		
Sunday		
Total Bankings		

BANK DIRECT CREDITS/DEBITS

Credits:		
Total Credits:		
Debits:		
Interest		
Finance Charges		
Cashed Cheques		
Total Debits:		

WEEK'S BANK BALANCE

£ at start of week		
+ Daily Bankings		
+ Direct Credits		
− Direct Debits		
− Chq. Payments		
Leaves: **Balance**		

BANK STATEMENT CHECK

Statement Balance		
Add any bankings		
Less any cheques (Not yet on Statement)		
Leaves: **Balance**		

PAYMENTS RECORD

	Ref	BY CASH £	p	BY CHEQUE £	p
Stock/Raw Materials					
Stock/Raw Materials Sub-Totals					
Employee Costs — Staff Wages					
Staff PAYE/NIC					
Premises Costs — Business Rent					
Business Rates					
Cleaning					
Electric/Gas/Heat/Water					
Property Insurance					
Repairs — Repairs/Maintenance					
General Admin. Expenses — Business Insurances					
Postage/Parcels					
Stationery/Printing					
Subscriptions					
Sundries					
Telephone/Fax					
Motor Expenses — Fuel					
Repairs/Service					
Tax/Insurance					
Travel & Subsistence					
Advertising & Promotion					
Legal & Professional — Fees (eg Solicitor or Accountant)					
Other Expenses					
Drawings/NIC					
CAPITAL EXPENDITURE					
Total Cash & Cheque Payments					

Week 12

commencing . . . .

PAYMENTS RECORD

	Ref	BY CASH £	p	BY CHEQUE £	p
Stock/Raw Materials					
Stock/Raw Materials Sub-Totals					
Employee Costs — Staff Wages					
Staff PAYE/NIC					
Premises Costs — Business Rent					
Business Rates					
Cleaning					
Electric/Gas/Heat/Water					
Property Insurance					
Repairs — Repairs/Maintenance					
General Admin. Expenses — Business Insurances					
Postage/Parcels					
Stationery/Printing					
Subscriptions					
Sundries					
Telephone/Fax					
Motor Expenses — Fuel					
Repairs/Service					
Tax/Insurance					
Travel & Subsistence					
Advertising & Promotion					
Legal & Professional — Fees (eg Solicitor or Accountant)					
Other Expenses					
Drawings/NIC					
CAPITAL EXPENDITURE					
Total Cash & Cheque Payments					

MONEY RECORD

Money in hand at start of week	£	p

DAILY TAKINGS		
Monday		
Tuesday		
Wednesday		
Thursday		
Friday		
Saturday		
Sunday		
Total Takings		

OTHER MONEY, LOANS etc		
Cash from Bank		
Total		

WEEK'S MONEY BALANCE		
£ at start of week		
+ Daily Takings		
+ Other Money		
− Daily Bankings		
− Cash Payments		
Leaves: Balance		

Money in hand at end of week		

Discrepancy ±		

© P. Hingston

BANK RECORD

Bank Balance at start of week	£	p

DAILY BANKINGS		
Monday		
Tuesday		
Wednesday		
Thursday		
Friday		
Saturday		
Sunday		
Total Bankings		

BANK DIRECT CREDITS/DEBITS		
Credits:		
Total Credits:		
Debits:		
Interest		
Finance Charges		
Cashed Cheques		
Total Debits:		

WEEK'S BANK BALANCE		
£ at start of week		
+ Daily Bankings		
+ Direct Credits		
− Direct Debits		
− Chq. Payments		
Leaves: Balance		

BANK STATEMENT CHECK		
Statement Balance		
Add any bankings		
Less any cheques (Not yet on Statement)		
Leaves: Balance		

Week 13

commencing..............................

PAYMENTS RECORD

	Ref	BY CASH £	p	BY CHEQUE £	p
Stock/Raw Materials					
Stock/Raw Materials Sub-Totals					
Employee Costs — Staff Wages					
Employee Costs					
Employee Costs					
Employee Costs — Staff PAYE/NIC					
Premises Costs — Business Rent					
Premises Costs — Business Rates					
Premises Costs — Cleaning					
Premises Costs — Electric/Gas/Heat/Water					
Premises Costs — Property Insurance					
Repairs — Repairs/Maintenance					
General Admin. Expenses — Business Insurances					
General Admin. Expenses — Postage/Parcels					
General Admin. Expenses — Stationery/Printing					
General Admin. Expenses — Subscriptions					
General Admin. Expenses — Sundries					
General Admin. Expenses — Telephone/Fax					
Motor Expenses — Fuel					
Motor Expenses — Repairs/Service					
Motor Expenses — Tax/Insurance					
Travel & Subsistence					
Advertising & Promotion					
Legal & Professional — Fees (eg Solicitor or Accountant)					
Other Expenses					
Drawings/NIC					
CAPITAL EXPENDITURE					
Total Cash & Cheque Payments					

MONEY RECORD

	£	p
Money in hand at start of week		
DAILY TAKINGS		
Monday		
Tuesday		
Wednesday		
Thursday		
Friday		
Saturday		
Sunday		
Total Takings		
OTHER MONEY, LOANS etc		
Cash from Bank		
Total		

WEEK'S MONEY BALANCE		
£ at start of week		
+ Daily Takings		
+ Other Money		
− Daily Bankings		
− Cash Payments		
Leaves: Balance		
Money in hand at end of week		
Discrepancy ±		

© P. Hingston

BANK RECORD

	£	p
Bank Balance at start of week		
DAILY BANKINGS		
Monday		
Tuesday		
Wednesday		
Thursday		
Friday		
Saturday		
Sunday		
Total Bankings		
BANK DIRECT CREDITS/DEBITS		
Credits:		
Total Credits:		
Debits:		
Interest		
Finance Charges		
Cashed Cheques		
Total Debits:		

WEEK'S BANK BALANCE		
£ at start of week		
+ Daily Bankings		
+ Direct Credits		
− Direct Debits		
− Chq. Payments		
Leaves: Balance		

BANK STATEMENT CHECK		
Statement Balance		
Add any bankings		
Less any cheques (Not yet on Statement)		
Leaves: Balance		

Week **14**

commencing ....

MONEY RECORD

Money in hand at start of week	£	p

DAILY TAKINGS

Monday		
Tuesday		
Wednesday		
Thursday		
Friday		
Saturday		
Sunday		
Total Takings		

OTHER MONEY, LOANS etc

Cash from Bank		
Total		

WEEK'S MONEY BALANCE

£ at start of week		
+ Daily Takings		
+ Other Money		
− Daily Bankings		
− Cash Payments		
Leaves: **Balance**		

Money in hand at end of week		

Discrepancy ±		

© P. Hingston

BANK RECORD

Bank Balance at start of week	£	p

DAILY BANKINGS

Monday		
Tuesday		
Wednesday		
Thursday		
Friday		
Saturday		
Sunday		
Total Bankings		

BANK DIRECT CREDITS/DEBITS

Credits:		
Total Credits:		
Debits:		
Interest		
Finance Charges		
Cashed Cheques		
Total Debits:		

WEEK'S BANK BALANCE

£ at start of week		
+ Daily Bankings		
+ Direct Credits		
− Direct Debits		
− Chq. Payments		
Leaves: **Balance**		

BANK STATEMENT CHECK

Statement Balance		
Add any bankings		
Less any cheques (Not yet on Statement)		
Leaves: **Balance**		

PAYMENTS RECORD

		Ref	BY CASH £	p	BY CHEQUE £	p
Stock/Raw Materials						
Stock/Raw Materials Sub-Totals						
Employee Costs	Staff Wages					
	Staff PAYE/NIC					
Premises Costs	Business Rent					
	Business Rates					
	Cleaning					
	Electric/Gas/Heat/Water					
	Property Insurance					
Repairs	Repairs/Maintenance					
General Admin. Expenses	Business Insurances					
	Postage/Parcels					
	Stationery/Printing					
	Subscriptions					
	Sundries					
	Telephone/Fax					
Motor Expenses	Fuel					
	Repairs/Service					
	Tax/Insurance					
Travel & Subsistence						
Advertising & Promotion						
Legal & Professional	Fees (eg Solicitor or Accountant)					
Other Expenses						
Drawings/NIC						
CAPITAL EXPENDITURE						
Total Cash & Cheque Payments						

Week 15

commencing ....

MONEY RECORD

Money in hand at start of week	£	p

DAILY TAKINGS

Monday		
Tuesday		
Wednesday		
Thursday		
Friday		
Saturday		
Sunday		
Total Takings		

OTHER MONEY, LOANS etc

Cash from Bank		
Total		

WEEK'S MONEY BALANCE

£ at start of week		
+ Daily Takings		
+ Other Money		
− Daily Bankings		
− Cash Payments		
Leaves: **Balance**		
Money in hand at end of week		
Discrepancy ±		

BANK RECORD

Bank Balance at start of week	£	p

DAILY BANKINGS

Monday		
Tuesday		
Wednesday		
Thursday		
Friday		
Saturday		
Sunday		
Total Bankings		

BANK DIRECT CREDITS/DEBITS

Credits:		
Total Credits:		
Debits:		
Interest		
Finance Charges		
Cashed Cheques		
Total Debits:		

WEEK'S BANK BALANCE

£ at start of week		
+ Daily Bankings		
+ Direct Credits		
− Direct Debits		
− Chq. Payments		
Leaves: **Balance**		

BANK STATEMENT CHECK

Statement Balance		
Add any bankings		
Less any cheques (Not yet on Statement)		
Leaves: **Balance**		

PAYMENTS RECORD

	Ref	BY CASH £	p	BY CHEQUE £	p
Stock/Raw Materials					
Stock/Raw Materials Sub-Totals					
Employee Costs — Staff Wages					
Staff PAYE/NIC					
Premises Costs — Business Rent					
Business Rates					
Cleaning					
Electric/Gas/Heat/Water					
Property Insurance					
Repairs — Repairs/Maintenance					
General Admin. Expenses — Business Insurances					
Postage/Parcels					
Stationery/Printing					
Subscriptions					
Sundries					
Telephone/Fax					
Motor Expenses — Fuel					
Repairs/Service					
Tax/Insurance					
Travel & Subsistence					
Advertising & Promotion					
Legal & Professional — Fees (eg Solicitor or Accountant)					
Other Expenses					
Drawings/NIC					
CAPITAL EXPENDITURE					
Total Cash & Cheque Payments					

Week **16**

commencing . . . .

MONEY RECORD

Money in hand at start of week	£	p

DAILY TAKINGS		
Monday		
Tuesday		
Wednesday		
Thursday		
Friday		
Saturday		
Sunday		
Total Takings		

OTHER MONEY, LOANS etc		
Cash from Bank		
Total		

WEEK'S MONEY BALANCE		
£ at start of week		
+ Daily Takings		
+ Other Money		
– Daily Bankings		
– Cash Payments		
Leaves: **Balance**		

Money in hand at end of week		

Discrepancy ±		

© P. Hingston

BANK RECORD

Bank Balance at start of week	£	p

DAILY BANKINGS		
Monday		
Tuesday		
Wednesday		
Thursday		
Friday		
Saturday		
Sunday		
Total Bankings		

BANK DIRECT CREDITS/DEBITS		
Credits:		
Total Credits:		
Debits:		
Interest		
Finance Charges		
Cashed Cheques		
Total Debits:		

WEEK'S BANK BALANCE		
£ at start of week		
+ Daily Bankings		
+ Direct Credits		
– Direct Debits		
– Chq. Payments		
Leaves: **Balance**		

BANK STATEMENT CHECK		
Statement Balance		
Add any bankings		
Less any cheques (Not yet on Statement)		
Leaves: **Balance**		

PAYMENTS RECORD

	Ref	BY CASH £	p	BY CHEQUE £	p
Stock/Raw Materials					
Stock/Raw Materials Sub-Totals					
Employee Costs — Staff Wages					
Staff PAYE/NIC					
Premises Costs — Business Rent					
Business Rates					
Cleaning					
Electric/Gas/Heat/Water					
Property Insurance					
Repairs — Repairs/Maintenance					
General Admin. Expenses — Business Insurances					
Postage/Parcels					
Stationery/Printing					
Subscriptions					
Sundries					
Telephone/Fax					
Motor Expenses — Fuel					
Repairs/Service					
Tax/Insurance					
Travel & Subsistence					
Advertising & Promotion					
Legal & Professional — Fees (eg Solicitor or Accountant)					
Other Expenses					
Drawings/NIC					
CAPITAL EXPENDITURE					
Total Cash & Cheque Payments					

Week 17

commencing ....

MONEY RECORD

BANK RECORD

PAYMENTS RECORD

	Ref	BY CASH £	p	BY CHEQUE £	p
Stock/Raw Materials					
Stock/Raw Materials Sub-Totals					

MONEY RECORD

	£	p
Money in hand at start of week		

DAILY TAKINGS		
Monday		
Tuesday		
Wednesday		
Thursday		
Friday		
Saturday		
Sunday		
Total Takings		

OTHER MONEY, LOANS etc		
Cash from Bank		
Total		

WEEK'S MONEY BALANCE		
£ at start of week		
+ Daily Takings		
+ Other Money		
− Daily Bankings		
− Cash Payments		
Leaves: Balance		

Money in hand at end of week		

Discrepancy ±		

© P. Hingston

BANK RECORD

	£	p
Bank Balance at start of week		

DAILY BANKINGS		
Monday		
Tuesday		
Wednesday		
Thursday		
Friday		
Saturday		
Sunday		
Total Bankings		

BANK DIRECT CREDITS/DEBITS		
Credits:		
Total Credits:		
Debits:		
Interest		
Finance Charges		
Cashed Cheques		
Total Debits:		

WEEK'S BANK BALANCE		
£ at start of week		
+ Daily Bankings		
+ Direct Credits		
− Direct Debits		
− Chq. Payments		
Leaves: Balance		

BANK STATEMENT CHECK		
Statement Balance		
Add any bankings Less any cheques (Not yet on Statement)		
Leaves: Balance		

PAYMENTS RECORD (continued)

		Ref	BY CASH £	p	BY CHEQUE £	p
Employee Costs	Staff Wages					
	Staff PAYE/NIC					
Premises Costs	Business Rent					
	Business Rates					
	Cleaning					
	Electric/Gas/Heat/Water					
	Property Insurance					
Repairs	Repairs/Maintenance					
General Admin. Expenses	Business Insurances					
	Postage/Parcels					
	Stationery/Printing					
	Subscriptions					
	Sundries					
	Telephone/Fax					
Motor Expenses	Fuel					
	Repairs/Service					
	Tax/Insurance					
Travel & Subsistence						
Advertising & Promotion						
Legal & Professional	Fees (eg Solicitor or Accountant)					
Other Expenses						
Drawings/NIC						
CAPITAL EXPENDITURE						
Total Cash & Cheque Payments						

Week 18

commencing . . . .

MONEY RECORD

Money in hand at start of week	£	p
DAILY TAKINGS		
Monday		
Tuesday		
Wednesday		
Thursday		
Friday		
Saturday		
Sunday		
Total Takings		

OTHER MONEY, LOANS etc		
Cash from Bank		
Total		

WEEK'S MONEY BALANCE		
£ at start of week		
+ Daily Takings		
+ Other Money		
− Daily Bankings		
− Cash Payments		
Leaves: **Balance**		

Money in hand at end of week		
Discrepancy ±		

© P. Hingston

BANK RECORD

Bank Balance at start of week	£	p
DAILY BANKINGS		
Monday		
Tuesday		
Wednesday		
Thursday		
Friday		
Saturday		
Sunday		
Total Bankings		

BANK DIRECT CREDITS/DEBITS		
Credits:		
Total Credits:		
Debits:		
Interest		
Finance Charges		
Cashed Cheques		
Total Debits:		

WEEK'S BANK BALANCE		
£ at start of week		
+ Daily Bankings		
+ Direct Credits		
− Direct Debits		
− Chq. Payments		
Leaves: **Balance**		

BANK STATEMENT CHECK		
Statement Balance		
Add any bankings Less any cheques (Not yet on Statement)		
Leaves: **Balance**		

PAYMENTS RECORD

	Ref	BY CASH £	p	BY CHEQUE £	p
Stock/Raw Materials					
Stock/Raw Materials Sub-Totals					
Employee Costs — Staff Wages					
Staff PAYE/NIC					
Premises Costs — Business Rent					
Business Rates					
Cleaning					
Electric/Gas/Heat/Water					
Property Insurance					
Repairs — Repairs/Maintenance					
General Admin. Expenses — Business Insurances					
Postage/Parcels					
Stationery/Printing					
Subscriptions					
Sundries					
Telephone/Fax					
Motor Expenses — Fuel					
Repairs/Service					
Tax/Insurance					
Travel & Subsistence					
Advertising & Promotion					
Legal & Professional — Fees (eg Solicitor or Accountant)					
Other Expenses					
Drawings/NIC					
CAPITAL EXPENDITURE					
Total Cash & Cheque Payments					

Week 19

commencing...........................

MONEY RECORD

Money in hand at start of week	£	p

DAILY TAKINGS

Monday		
Tuesday		
Wednesday		
Thursday		
Friday		
Saturday		
Sunday		
Total Takings		

OTHER MONEY, LOANS etc

Cash from Bank		
Total		

WEEK'S MONEY BALANCE

£ at start of week		
+ Daily Takings		
+ Other Money		
− Daily Bankings		
− Cash Payments		
Leaves: **Balance**		

Money in hand at end of week		

Discrepancy ±		

© P. Hingston

BANK RECORD

Bank Balance at start of week	£	p

DAILY BANKINGS

Monday		
Tuesday		
Wednesday		
Thursday		
Friday		
Saturday		
Sunday		
Total Bankings		

BANK DIRECT CREDITS/DEBITS

Credits:		
Total Credits:		
Debits:		
Interest		
Finance Charges		
Cashed Cheques		
Total Debits:		

WEEK'S BANK BALANCE

£ at start of week		
+ Daily Bankings		
+ Direct Credits		
− Direct Debits		
− Chq. Payments		
Leaves: **Balance**		

BANK STATEMENT CHECK

Statement Balance		
Add any bankings		
Less any cheques (Not yet on Statement)		
Leaves: **Balance**		

PAYMENTS RECORD

	Ref	BY CASH £ p		BY CHEQUE £ p	
Stock/Raw Materials					
Stock/Raw Materials Sub-Totals					
Employee Costs — Staff Wages					
Employee Costs — Staff PAYE/NIC					
Premises Costs — Business Rent					
Premises Costs — Business Rates					
Premises Costs — Cleaning					
Premises Costs — Electric/Gas/Heat/Water					
Premises Costs — Property Insurance					
Repairs — Repairs/Maintenance					
General Admin. Expenses — Business Insurances					
General Admin. Expenses — Postage/Parcels					
General Admin. Expenses — Stationery/Printing					
General Admin. Expenses — Subscriptions					
General Admin. Expenses — Sundries					
General Admin. Expenses — Telephone/Fax					
Motor Expenses — Fuel					
Motor Expenses — Repairs/Service					
Motor Expenses — Tax/Insurance					
Travel & Subsistence					
Advertising & Promotion					
Legal & Professional — Fees (eg Solicitor or Accountant)					
Other Expenses					
Drawings/NIC					
CAPITAL EXPENDITURE					
Total Cash & Cheque Payments					

Week **20**

commencing . . . .

MONEY RECORD

Money in hand at start of week	£	p
DAILY TAKINGS		
Monday		
Tuesday		
Wednesday		
Thursday		
Friday		
Saturday		
Sunday		
Total Takings		

OTHER MONEY, LOANS etc		
Cash from Bank		
Total		

WEEK'S MONEY BALANCE		
£ at start of week		
+ Daily Takings		
+ Other Money		
− Daily Bankings		
− Cash Payments		
Leaves: **Balance**		

Money in hand at end of week		

Discrepancy ±		

© P. Hingston

BANK RECORD

Bank Balance at start of week	£	p
DAILY BANKINGS		
Monday		
Tuesday		
Wednesday		
Thursday		
Friday		
Saturday		
Sunday		
Total Bankings		

BANK DIRECT CREDITS/DEBITS		
Credits:		
Total Credits:		
Debits:		
Interest		
Finance Charges		
Cashed Cheques		
Total Debits:		

WEEK'S BANK BALANCE		
£ at start of week		
+ Daily Bankings		
+ Direct Credits		
− Direct Debits		
− Chq. Payments		
Leaves: **Balance**		

BANK STATEMENT CHECK		
Statement Balance		
Add any bankings		
Less any cheques (Not yet on Statement)		
Leaves: **Balance**		

PAYMENTS RECORD

	Ref	BY CASH £	p	BY CHEQUE £	p
Stock/Raw Materials					
Stock/Raw Materials Sub-Totals					
Employee Costs — Staff Wages					
Staff PAYE/NIC					
Premises Costs — Business Rent					
Business Rates					
Cleaning					
Electric/Gas/Heat/Water					
Property Insurance					
Repairs — Repairs/Maintenance					
General Admin. Expenses — Business Insurances					
Postage/Parcels					
Stationery/Printing					
Subscriptions					
Sundries					
Telephone/Fax					
Motor Expenses — Fuel					
Repairs/Service					
Tax/Insurance					
Travel & Subsistence					
Advertising & Promotion					
Legal & Professional — Fees (eg Solicitor or Accountant)					
Other Expenses					
Drawings/NIC					
CAPITAL EXPENDITURE					
Total Cash & Cheque Payments					

Week 21

commencing . . . .

MONEY RECORD

	£	p
Money in hand at start of week		

DAILY TAKINGS		
Monday		
Tuesday		
Wednesday		
Thursday		
Friday		
Saturday		
Sunday		
Total Takings		

OTHER MONEY, LOANS etc		
Cash from Bank		
Total		

WEEK'S MONEY BALANCE		
£ at start of week		
+ Daily Takings		
+ Other Money		
− Daily Bankings		
− Cash Payments		
Leaves: **Balance**		
Money in hand at end of week		
Discrepancy ±		

© P. Hingston

BANK RECORD

	£	p
Bank Balance at start of week		

DAILY BANKINGS		
Monday		
Tuesday		
Wednesday		
Thursday		
Friday		
Saturday		
Sunday		
Total Bankings		

BANK DIRECT CREDITS/DEBITS		
Credits:		
Total Credits:		
Debits:		
Interest		
Finance Charges		
Cashed Cheques		
Total Debits:		

WEEK'S BANK BALANCE		
£ at start of week		
+ Daily Bankings		
+ Direct Credits		
− Direct Debits		
− Chq. Payments		
Leaves: **Balance**		

BANK STATEMENT CHECK		
Statement Balance		
Add any bankings		
Less any cheques (Not yet on Statement)		
Leaves: **Balance**		

PAYMENTS RECORD

		Ref	BY CASH £	p	BY CHEQUE £	p
Stock/Raw Materials						
Stock/Raw Materials Sub-Totals						
Employee Costs	Staff Wages					
	Staff PAYE/NIC					
Premises Costs	Business Rent					
	Business Rates					
	Cleaning					
	Electric/Gas/Heat/Water					
	Property Insurance					
Repairs	Repairs/Maintenance					
General Admin. Expenses	Business Insurances					
	Postage/Parcels					
	Stationery/Printing					
	Subscriptions					
	Sundries					
	Telephone/Fax					
Motor Expenses	Fuel					
	Repairs/Service					
	Tax/Insurance					
Travel & Subsistence						
Advertising & Promotion						
Legal & Professional	Fees (eg Solicitor or Accountant)					
Other Expenses						
Drawings/NIC						
CAPITAL EXPENDITURE						
Total Cash & Cheque Payments						

Week 22

commencing . . . .

MONEY RECORD

Money in hand at start of week	£	p

DAILY TAKINGS

Monday		
Tuesday		
Wednesday		
Thursday		
Friday		
Saturday		
Sunday		
Total Takings		

OTHER MONEY, LOANS etc

Cash from Bank		
Total		

WEEK'S MONEY BALANCE

£ at start of week		
+ Daily Takings		
+ Other Money		
− Daily Bankings		
− Cash Payments		
Leaves: **Balance**		

Money in hand at end of week		

Discrepancy ±		

© P. Hingston

BANK RECORD

Bank Balance at start of week	£	p

DAILY BANKINGS

Monday		
Tuesday		
Wednesday		
Thursday		
Friday		
Saturday		
Sunday		
Total Bankings		

BANK DIRECT CREDITS/DEBITS

Credits:		
Total Credits:		
Debits:		
Interest		
Finance Charges		
Cashed Cheques		
Total Debits:		

WEEK'S BANK BALANCE

£ at start of week		
+ Daily Bankings		
+ Direct Credits		
− Direct Debits		
− Chq. Payments		
Leaves: **Balance**		

BANK STATEMENT CHECK

Statement Balance		
Add any bankings Less any cheques (Not yet on Statement)		
Leaves: **Balance**		

PAYMENTS RECORD

	Ref	BY CASH £	p	BY CHEQUE £	p
Stock/Raw Materials					
Stock/Raw Materials Sub-Totals					
Employee Costs	Staff Wages				
	Staff PAYE/NIC				
Premises Costs	Business Rent				
	Business Rates				
	Cleaning				
	Electric/Gas/Heat/Water				
	Property Insurance				
Repairs	Repairs/Maintenance				
General Admin. Expenses	Business Insurances				
	Postage/Parcels				
	Stationery/Printing				
	Subscriptions				
	Sundries				
	Telephone/Fax				
Motor Expenses	Fuel				
	Repairs/Service				
	Tax/Insurance				
Travel & Subsistence					
Advertising & Promotion					
Legal & Professional	Fees (eg Solicitor or Accountant)				
Other Expenses					
Drawings/NIC					
CAPITAL EXPENDITURE					
Total Cash & Cheque Payments					

Week 23

commencing . . . .

MONEY RECORD

Money in hand at start of week	£	p

DAILY TAKINGS		
Monday		
Tuesday		
Wednesday		
Thursday		
Friday		
Saturday		
Sunday		
Total Takings		

OTHER MONEY, LOANS etc		
Cash from Bank		
Total		

WEEK'S MONEY BALANCE		
£ at start of week		
+ Daily Takings		
+ Other Money		
− Daily Bankings		
− Cash Payments		
Leaves: Balance		

Money in hand at end of week		

Discrepancy ±		

© P. Hingston

BANK RECORD

Bank Balance at start of week	£	p

DAILY BANKINGS		
Monday		
Tuesday		
Wednesday		
Thursday		
Friday		
Saturday		
Sunday		
Total Bankings		

BANK DIRECT CREDITS/DEBITS		
Credits:		
Total Credits:		
Debits:		
Interest		
Finance Charges		
Cashed Cheques		
Total Debits:		

WEEK'S BANK BALANCE		
£ at start of week		
+ Daily Bankings		
+ Direct Credits		
− Direct Debits		
− Chq. Payments		
Leaves: Balance		

BANK STATEMENT CHECK		
Statement Balance		
Add any bankings Less any cheques (Not yet on Statement)		
Leaves: Balance		

PAYMENTS RECORD

	Ref	BY CASH £	p	BY CHEQUE £	p
Stock/Raw Materials					
Stock/Raw Materials Sub-Totals					
Employee Costs — Staff Wages					
Staff PAYE/NIC					
Premises Costs — Business Rent					
Business Rates					
Cleaning					
Electric/Gas/Heat/Water					
Property Insurance					
Repairs — Repairs/Maintenance					
General Admin. Expenses — Business Insurances					
Postage/Parcels					
Stationery/Printing					
Subscriptions					
Sundries					
Telephone/Fax					
Motor Expenses — Fuel					
Repairs/Service					
Tax/Insurance					
Travel & Subsistence					
Advertising & Promotion					
Legal & Professional — Fees (eg Solicitor or Accountant)					
Other Expenses					
Drawings/NIC					
CAPITAL EXPENDITURE					
Total Cash & Cheque Payments					

Week **24**

commencing . . . .

MONEY RECORD

Money in hand at start of week	£	p

DAILY TAKINGS		
Monday		
Tuesday		
Wednesday		
Thursday		
Friday		
Saturday		
Sunday		
Total Takings		

OTHER MONEY, LOANS etc		
Cash from Bank		
Total		

WEEK'S MONEY BALANCE		
£ at start of week		
+ Daily Takings		
+ Other Money		
− Daily Bankings		
− Cash Payments		
Leaves: **Balance**		

Money in hand at end of week		

Discrepancy ±		

© P. Hingston

BANK RECORD

Bank Balance at start of week	£	p

DAILY BANKINGS		
Monday		
Tuesday		
Wednesday		
Thursday		
Friday		
Saturday		
Sunday		
Total Bankings		

BANK DIRECT CREDITS/DEBITS		
Credits:		
Total Credits:		
Debits:		
Interest		
Finance Charges		
Cashed Cheques		
Total Debits:		

WEEK'S BANK BALANCE		
£ at start of week		
+ Daily Bankings		
+ Direct Credits		
− Direct Debits		
− Chq. Payments		
Leaves: **Balance**		

BANK STATEMENT CHECK		
Statement Balance		
Add any bankings		
Less any cheques (Not yet on Statement)		
Leaves: **Balance**		

PAYMENTS RECORD

	Ref	BY CASH £	p	BY CHEQUE £	p
Stock/Raw Materials					
Stock/Raw Materials Sub-Totals					
Employee Costs — Staff Wages					
Staff PAYE/NIC					
Premises Costs — Business Rent					
Business Rates					
Cleaning					
Electric/Gas/Heat/Water					
Property Insurance					
Repairs — Repairs/Maintenance					
General Admin. Expenses — Business Insurances					
Postage/Parcels					
Stationery/Printing					
Subscriptions					
Sundries					
Telephone/Fax					
Motor Expenses — Fuel					
Repairs/Service					
Tax/Insurance					
Travel & Subsistence					
Advertising & Promotion					
Legal & Professional — Fees (eg Solicitor or Accountant)					
Other Expenses					
Drawings/NIC					
CAPITAL EXPENDITURE					
Total Cash & Cheque Payments					

Week 25

commencing . . . .

MONEY RECORD

Money in hand at start of week	£	p

DAILY TAKINGS		
Monday		
Tuesday		
Wednesday		
Thursday		
Friday		
Saturday		
Sunday		
Total Takings		

OTHER MONEY, LOANS etc		
Cash from Bank		
Total		

WEEK'S MONEY BALANCE		
£ at start of week		
+ Daily Takings		
+ Other Money		
− Daily Bankings		
− Cash Payments		
Leaves: **Balance**		

Money in hand at end of week		

Discrepancy ±		

© P. Hingston

BANK RECORD

Bank Balance at start of week	£	p

DAILY BANKINGS		
Monday		
Tuesday		
Wednesday		
Thursday		
Friday		
Saturday		
Sunday		
Total Bankings		

BANK DIRECT CREDITS/DEBITS		
Credits:		
Total Credits:		
Debits:		
Interest		
Finance Charges		
Cashed Cheques		
Total Debits:		

WEEK'S BANK BALANCE		
£ at start of week		
+ Daily Bankings		
+ Direct Credits		
− Direct Debits		
− Chq. Payments		
Leaves: **Balance**		

BANK STATEMENT CHECK		
Statement Balance		
Add any bankings		
Less any cheques (Not yet on Statement)		
Leaves: **Balance**		

PAYMENTS RECORD

		Ref	BY CASH £	p	BY CHEQUE £	p
Stock/Raw Materials						
Stock/Raw Materials Sub-Totals						
Employee Costs	Staff Wages					
	Staff PAYE/NIC					
Premises Costs	Business Rent					
	Business Rates					
	Cleaning					
	Electric/Gas/Heat/Water					
	Property Insurance					
Repairs	Repairs/Maintenance					
General Admin. Expenses	Business Insurances					
	Postage/Parcels					
	Stationery/Printing					
	Subscriptions					
	Sundries					
	Telephone/Fax					
Motor Expenses	Fuel					
	Repairs/Service					
	Tax/Insurance					
Travel & Subsistence						
Advertising & Promotion						
Legal & Professional	Fees (eg Solicitor or Accountant)					
Other Expenses						
Drawings/NIC						
CAPITAL EXPENDITURE						
Total Cash & Cheque Payments						

Week 26

commencing . . . .

MONEY RECORD

	£	p
Money in hand at start of week		
DAILY TAKINGS		
Monday		
Tuesday		
Wednesday		
Thursday		
Friday		
Saturday		
Sunday		
Total Takings		
OTHER MONEY, LOANS etc		
Cash from Bank		
Total		

WEEK'S MONEY BALANCE

	£	p
£ at start of week		
+ Daily Takings		
+ Other Money		
− Daily Bankings		
− Cash Payments		
Leaves: **Balance**		
Money in hand at end of week		
Discrepancy ±		

BANK RECORD

	£	p
Bank Balance at start of week		
DAILY BANKINGS		
Monday		
Tuesday		
Wednesday		
Thursday		
Friday		
Saturday		
Sunday		
Total Bankings		
BANK DIRECT CREDITS/DEBITS		
Credits:		
Total Credits:		
Debits:		
Interest		
Finance Charges		
Cashed Cheques		
Total Debits:		

WEEK'S BANK BALANCE

	£	p
£ at start of week		
+ Daily Bankings		
+ Direct Credits		
− Direct Debits		
− Chq. Payments		
Leaves: **Balance**		

BANK STATEMENT CHECK

	£	p
Statement Balance		
Add any bankings		
Less any cheques (Not yet on Statement)		
Leaves: **Balance**		

© P. Hingston

PAYMENTS RECORD

		Ref	BY CASH £	p	BY CHEQUE £	p
Stock/Raw Materials						
Stock/Raw Materials Sub-Totals						
Employee Costs	Staff Wages					
	Staff PAYE/NIC					
Premises Costs	Business Rent					
	Business Rates					
	Cleaning					
	Electric/Gas/Heat/Water					
	Property Insurance					
Repairs	Repairs/Maintenance					
General Admin. Expenses	Business Insurances					
	Postage/Parcels					
	Stationery/Printing					
	Subscriptions					
	Sundries					
	Telephone/Fax					
Motor Expenses	Fuel					
	Repairs/Service					
	Tax/Insurance					
Travel & Subsistence						
Advertising & Promotion						
Legal & Professional	Fees (eg Solicitor or Accountant)					
Other Expenses						
Drawings/NIC						
CAPITAL EXPENDITURE						
Total Cash & Cheque Payments						

Week 27

commencing ....

MONEY RECORD

Money in hand at start of week	£	p

DAILY TAKINGS		
Monday		
Tuesday		
Wednesday		
Thursday		
Friday		
Saturday		
Sunday		
Total Takings		

OTHER MONEY, LOANS etc		
Cash from Bank		
Total		

WEEK'S MONEY BALANCE		
£ at start of week		
+ Daily Takings		
+ Other Money		
– Daily Bankings		
– Cash Payments		
Leaves: **Balance**		

Money in hand at end of week		

Discrepancy ±		

© P. Hingston

BANK RECORD

Bank Balance at start of week	£	p

DAILY BANKINGS		
Monday		
Tuesday		
Wednesday		
Thursday		
Friday		
Saturday		
Sunday		
Total Bankings		

BANK DIRECT CREDITS/DEBITS		
Credits:		
Total Credits:		
Debits:		
Interest		
Finance Charges		
Cashed Cheques		
Total Debits:		

WEEK'S BANK BALANCE		
£ at start of week		
+ Daily Bankings		
+ Direct Credits		
– Direct Debits		
– Chq. Payments		
Leaves: **Balance**		

BANK STATEMENT CHECK		
Statement Balance		
Add any bankings		
Less any cheques (Not yet on Statement)		
Leaves: **Balance**		

PAYMENTS RECORD

	Ref	BY CASH £	p	BY CHEQUE £	p
Stock/Raw Materials					
Stock/Raw Materials Sub-Totals					
Employee Costs — Staff Wages					
Employee Costs					
Employee Costs					
Staff PAYE/NIC					
Premises Costs — Business Rent					
Business Rates					
Cleaning					
Electric/Gas/Heat/Water					
Property Insurance					
Repairs — Repairs/Maintenance					
General Admin. Expenses — Business Insurances					
Postage/Parcels					
Stationery/Printing					
Subscriptions					
Sundries					
Telephone/Fax					
Motor Expenses — Fuel					
Repairs/Service					
Tax/Insurance					
Travel & Subsistence					
Advertising & Promotion					
Legal & Professional — Fees (eg Solicitor or Accountant)					
Other Expenses					
Drawings/NIC					
CAPITAL EXPENDITURE					
Total Cash & Cheque Payments					

Week **28**

commencing . . . .

MONEY RECORD

Money in hand at start of week	£	p
DAILY TAKINGS		
Monday		
Tuesday		
Wednesday		
Thursday		
Friday		
Saturday		
Sunday		
Total Takings		
OTHER MONEY, LOANS etc		
Cash from Bank		
Total		

WEEK'S MONEY BALANCE		
£ at start of week		
+ Daily Takings		
+ Other Money		
− Daily Bankings		
− Cash Payments		
Leaves: **Balance**		
Money in hand at end of week		
Discrepancy ±		

© P. Hingston

BANK RECORD

Bank Balance at start of week	£	p
DAILY BANKINGS		
Monday		
Tuesday		
Wednesday		
Thursday		
Friday		
Saturday		
Sunday		
Total Bankings		
BANK DIRECT CREDITS/DEBITS		
Credits:		
Total Credits:		
Debits:		
Interest		
Finance Charges		
Cashed Cheques		
Total Debits:		

WEEK'S BANK BALANCE		
£ at start of week		
+ Daily Bankings		
+ Direct Credits		
− Direct Debits		
− Chq. Payments		
Leaves: **Balance**		

BANK STATEMENT CHECK		
Statement Balance		
Add any bankings Less any cheques (Not yet on Statement)		
Leaves: **Balance**		

PAYMENTS RECORD

		Ref	BY CASH £	p	BY CHEQUE £	p
Stock/Raw Materials						
Stock/Raw Materials Sub-Totals						
Employee Costs	Staff Wages					
	Staff PAYE/NIC					
Premises Costs	Business Rent					
	Business Rates					
	Cleaning					
	Electric/Gas/Heat/Water					
	Property Insurance					
Repairs	Repairs/Maintenance					
General Admin. Expenses	Business Insurances					
	Postage/Parcels					
	Stationery/Printing					
	Subscriptions					
	Sundries					
	Telephone/Fax					
Motor Expenses	Fuel					
	Repairs/Service					
	Tax/Insurance					
Travel & Subsistence						
Advertising & Promotion						
Legal & Professional	Fees (eg Solicitor or Accountant)					
Other Expenses						
Drawings/NIC						
CAPITAL EXPENDITURE						
Total Cash & Cheque Payments						

Week 29

commencing . . . .

MONEY RECORD

Money in hand at start of week	£	p

DAILY TAKINGS		
Monday		
Tuesday		
Wednesday		
Thursday		
Friday		
Saturday		
Sunday		
Total Takings		

OTHER MONEY, LOANS etc		
Cash from Bank		
Total		

WEEK'S MONEY BALANCE		
£ at start of week		
+ Daily Takings		
+ Other Money		
– Daily Bankings		
– Cash Payments		
Leaves: Balance		
Money in hand at end of week		
Discrepancy ±		

© P. Hingston

BANK RECORD

Bank Balance at start of week	£	p

DAILY BANKINGS		
Monday		
Tuesday		
Wednesday		
Thursday		
Friday		
Saturday		
Sunday		
Total Bankings		

BANK DIRECT CREDITS/DEBITS		
Credits:		
Total Credits:		
Debits:		
Interest		
Finance Charges		
Cashed Cheques		
Total Debits:		

WEEK'S BANK BALANCE		
£ at start of week		
+ Daily Bankings		
+ Direct Credits		
– Direct Debits		
– Chq. Payments		
Leaves: Balance		

BANK STATEMENT CHECK		
Statement Balance		
Add any bankings		
Less any cheques (Not yet on Statement)		
Leaves: Balance		

PAYMENTS RECORD

	Ref	BY CASH £	p	BY CHEQUE £	p
Stock/Raw Materials					
Stock/Raw Materials Sub-Totals					
Employee Costs — Staff Wages					
Staff PAYE/NIC					
Premises Costs — Business Rent					
Business Rates					
Cleaning					
Electric/Gas/Heat/Water					
Property Insurance					
Repairs — Repairs/Maintenance					
General Admin. Expenses — Business Insurances					
Postage/Parcels					
Stationery/Printing					
Subscriptions					
Sundries					
Telephone/Fax					
Motor Expenses — Fuel					
Repairs/Service					
Tax/Insurance					
Travel & Subsistence					
Advertising & Promotion					
Legal & Professional — Fees (eg Solicitor or Accountant)					
Other Expenses					
Drawings/NIC					
CAPITAL EXPENDITURE					
Total Cash & Cheque Payments					

Week **30**

commencing . . . .

MONEY RECORD

Money in hand at start of week	£	p

DAILY TAKINGS

Monday		
Tuesday		
Wednesday		
Thursday		
Friday		
Saturday		
Sunday		
Total Takings		

OTHER MONEY, LOANS etc

Cash from Bank		
Total		

WEEK'S MONEY BALANCE

£ at start of week		
+ Daily Takings		
+ Other Money		
− Daily Bankings		
− Cash Payments		
Leaves: **Balance**		

Money in hand at end of week		

Discrepancy ±		

© P. Hingston

BANK RECORD

Bank Balance at start of week	£	p

DAILY BANKINGS

Monday		
Tuesday		
Wednesday		
Thursday		
Friday		
Saturday		
Sunday		
Total Bankings		

BANK DIRECT CREDITS/DEBITS

Credits:		
Total Credits:		
Debits:		
Interest		
Finance Charges		
Cashed Cheques		
Total Debits:		

WEEK'S BANK BALANCE

£ at start of week		
+ Daily Bankings		
+ Direct Credits		
− Direct Debits		
− Chq. Payments		
Leaves: **Balance**		

BANK STATEMENT CHECK

Statement Balance		
Add any bankings		
Less any cheques (Not yet on Statement)		
Leaves: **Balance**		

PAYMENTS RECORD

	Ref	BY CASH £	p	BY CHEQUE £	p
Stock/Raw Materials					
Stock/Raw Materials Sub-Totals					
Employee Costs	Staff Wages				
	Staff PAYE/NIC				
Premises Costs	Business Rent				
	Business Rates				
	Cleaning				
	Electric/Gas/Heat/Water				
	Property Insurance				
Repairs	Repairs/Maintenance				
General Admin. Expenses	Business Insurances				
	Postage/Parcels				
	Stationery/Printing				
	Subscriptions				
	Sundries				
	Telephone/Fax				
Motor Expenses	Fuel				
	Repairs/Service				
	Tax/Insurance				
Travel & Subsistence					
Advertising & Promotion					
Legal & Professional	Fees (eg Solicitor or Accountant)				
Other Expenses					
Drawings/NIC					
CAPITAL EXPENDITURE					
Total Cash & Cheque Payments					

Week 31

commencing ....

MONEY RECORD

Money in hand at start of week	£	p

DAILY TAKINGS

Monday		
Tuesday		
Wednesday		
Thursday		
Friday		
Saturday		
Sunday		
Total Takings		

OTHER MONEY, LOANS etc

Cash from Bank		
Total		

WEEK'S MONEY BALANCE

£ at start of week		
+ Daily Takings		
+ Other Money		
− Daily Bankings		
− Cash Payments		
Leaves: Balance		

Money in hand at end of week		

Discrepancy ±		

© P. Hingston

BANK RECORD

Bank Balance at start of week	£	p

DAILY BANKINGS

Monday		
Tuesday		
Wednesday		
Thursday		
Friday		
Saturday		
Sunday		
Total Bankings		

BANK DIRECT CREDITS/DEBITS

Credits:		
Total Credits:		
Debits:		
Interest		
Finance Charges		
Cashed Cheques		
Total Debits:		

WEEK'S BANK BALANCE

£ at start of week		
+ Daily Bankings		
+ Direct Credits		
− Direct Debits		
− Chq. Payments		
Leaves: Balance		

BANK STATEMENT CHECK

Statement Balance		
Add any bankings		
Less any cheques (Not yet on Statement)		
Leaves: Balance		

PAYMENTS RECORD

	Ref	BY CASH £	p	BY CHEQUE £	p
Stock/Raw Materials					
Stock/Raw Materials Sub-Totals					
Employee Costs — Staff Wages					
Staff PAYE/NIC					
Premises Costs — Business Rent					
Business Rates					
Cleaning					
Electric/Gas/Heat/Water					
Property Insurance					
Repairs — Repairs/Maintenance					
General Admin. Expenses — Business Insurances					
Postage/Parcels					
Stationery/Printing					
Subscriptions					
Sundries					
Telephone/Fax					
Motor Expenses — Fuel					
Repairs/Service					
Tax/Insurance					
Travel & Subsistence					
Advertising & Promotion					
Legal & Professional — Fees (eg Solicitor or Accountant)					
Other Expenses					
Drawings/NIC					
CAPITAL EXPENDITURE					
Total Cash & Cheque Payments					

Week 32

commencing.............................

MONEY RECORD

Money in hand at start of week	£	p

DAILY TAKINGS		
Monday		
Tuesday		
Wednesday		
Thursday		
Friday		
Saturday		
Sunday		
Total Takings		

OTHER MONEY, LOANS etc		
Cash from Bank		
Total		

WEEK'S MONEY BALANCE		
£ at start of week		
+ Daily Takings		
+ Other Money		
− Daily Bankings		
− Cash Payments		
Leaves: Balance		

Money in hand at end of week		

Discrepancy ±		

© P. Hingston

BANK RECORD

Bank Balance at start of week	£	p

DAILY BANKINGS		
Monday		
Tuesday		
Wednesday		
Thursday		
Friday		
Saturday		
Sunday		
Total Bankings		

BANK DIRECT CREDITS/DEBITS		
Credits:		
Total Credits:		
Debits:		
Interest		
Finance Charges		
Cashed Cheques		
Total Debits:		

WEEK'S BANK BALANCE		
£ at start of week		
+ Daily Bankings		
+ Direct Credits		
− Direct Debits		
− Chq. Payments		
Leaves: Balance		

BANK STATEMENT CHECK		
Statement Balance		
Add any bankings		
Less any cheques (Not yet on Statement)		
Leaves: Balance		

PAYMENTS RECORD

		Ref	BY CASH £	p	BY CHEQUE £	p
Stock/Raw Materials						
Stock/Raw Materials Sub-Totals						
Employee Costs	Staff Wages					
	Staff PAYE/NIC					
Premises Costs	Business Rent					
	Business Rates					
	Cleaning					
	Electric/Gas/Heat/Water					
	Property Insurance					
Repairs	Repairs/Maintenance					
General Admin. Expenses	Business Insurances					
	Postage/Parcels					
	Stationery/Printing					
	Subscriptions					
	Sundries					
	Telephone/Fax					
Motor Expenses	Fuel					
	Repairs/Service					
	Tax/Insurance					
Travel & Subsistence						
Advertising & Promotion						
Legal & Professional	Fees (eg Solicitor or Accountant)					
Other Expenses						
Drawings/NIC						
CAPITAL EXPENDITURE						
Total Cash & Cheque Payments						

Week 33

commencing ....

MONEY RECORD

Money in hand at start of week	£	p

DAILY TAKINGS		
Monday		
Tuesday		
Wednesday		
Thursday		
Friday		
Saturday		
Sunday		
Total Takings		

OTHER MONEY, LOANS etc		
Cash from Bank		
Total		

WEEK'S MONEY BALANCE		
£ at start of week		
+ Daily Takings		
+ Other Money		
– Daily Bankings		
– Cash Payments		
Leaves: **Balance**		

Money in hand at end of week		

Discrepancy ±		

© P. Hingston

BANK RECORD

Bank Balance at start of week	£	p

DAILY BANKINGS		
Monday		
Tuesday		
Wednesday		
Thursday		
Friday		
Saturday		
Sunday		
Total Bankings		

BANK DIRECT CREDITS/DEBITS		
Credits:		
Total Credits:		
Debits:		
Interest		
Finance Charges		
Cashed Cheques		
Total Debits:		

WEEK'S BANK BALANCE		
£ at start of week		
+ Daily Bankings		
+ Direct Credits		
– Direct Debits		
– Chq. Payments		
Leaves: **Balance**		

BANK STATEMENT CHECK		
Statement Balance		
Add any bankings Less any cheques (Not yet on Statement)		
Leaves: **Balance**		

PAYMENTS RECORD

		Ref	BY CASH £	p	BY CHEQUE £	p
Stock/Raw Materials						
Stock/Raw Materials Sub-Totals						
Employee Costs	Staff Wages					
	Staff PAYE/NIC					
Premises Costs	Business Rent					
	Business Rates					
	Cleaning					
	Electric/Gas/Heat/Water					
	Property Insurance					
Repairs	Repairs/Maintenance					
General Admin. Expenses	Business Insurances					
	Postage/Parcels					
	Stationery/Printing					
	Subscriptions					
	Sundries					
	Telephone/Fax					
Motor Expenses	Fuel					
	Repairs/Service					
	Tax/Insurance					
Travel & Subsistence						
Advertising & Promotion						
Legal & Professional	Fees (eg Solicitor or Accountant)					
Other Expenses						
Drawings/NIC						
CAPITAL EXPENDITURE						
Total Cash & Cheque Payments						

Week **34**

commencing . . . .

MONEY RECORD

Money in hand at start of week	£	p

DAILY TAKINGS		
Monday		
Tuesday		
Wednesday		
Thursday		
Friday		
Saturday		
Sunday		
Total Takings		

OTHER MONEY, LOANS etc		
Cash from Bank		
Total		

WEEK'S MONEY BALANCE		
£ at start of week		
+ Daily Takings		
+ Other Money		
− Daily Bankings		
− Cash Payments		
Leaves: Balance		

Money in hand at end of week		

Discrepancy ±		

© P. Hingston

BANK RECORD

Bank Balance at start of week	£	p

DAILY BANKINGS		
Monday		
Tuesday		
Wednesday		
Thursday		
Friday		
Saturday		
Sunday		
Total Bankings		

BANK DIRECT CREDITS/DEBITS		
Credits:		
Total Credits:		
Debits:		
Interest		
Finance Charges		
Cashed Cheques		
Total Debits:		

WEEK'S BANK BALANCE		
£ at start of week		
+ Daily Bankings		
+ Direct Credits		
− Direct Debits		
− Chq. Payments		
Leaves: Balance		

BANK STATEMENT CHECK		
Statement Balance		
Add any bankings		
Less any cheques (Not yet on Statement)		
Leaves: Balance		

PAYMENTS RECORD

	Ref	BY CASH £	p	BY CHEQUE £	p
Stock/Raw Materials					
Stock/Raw Materials Sub-Totals					
Employee Costs — Staff Wages					
Employee Costs — Staff PAYE/NIC					
Premises Costs — Business Rent					
Premises Costs — Business Rates					
Premises Costs — Cleaning					
Premises Costs — Electric/Gas/Heat/Water					
Premises Costs — Property Insurance					
Repairs — Repairs/Maintenance					
General Admin. Expenses — Business Insurances					
General Admin. Expenses — Postage/Parcels					
General Admin. Expenses — Stationery/Printing					
General Admin. Expenses — Subscriptions					
General Admin. Expenses — Sundries					
General Admin. Expenses — Telephone/Fax					
Motor Expenses — Fuel					
Motor Expenses — Repairs/Service					
Motor Expenses — Tax/Insurance					
Travel & Subsistence					
Advertising & Promotion					
Legal & Professional — Fees (eg Solicitor or Accountant)					
Other Expenses					
Drawings/NIC					
CAPITAL EXPENDITURE					
Total Cash & Cheque Payments					

Week **35**

commencing . . . .

MONEY RECORD

Money in hand at start of week	£	p

DAILY TAKINGS		
Monday		
Tuesday		
Wednesday		
Thursday		
Friday		
Saturday		
Sunday		
Total Takings		

OTHER MONEY, LOANS etc		
Cash from Bank		
Total		

WEEK'S MONEY BALANCE		
£ at start of week		
+ Daily Takings		
+ Other Money		
− Daily Bankings		
− Cash Payments		
Leaves: **Balance**		

Money in hand at end of week		

Discrepancy ±		

© P. Hingston

BANK RECORD

Bank Balance at start of week	£	p

DAILY BANKINGS		
Monday		
Tuesday		
Wednesday		
Thursday		
Friday		
Saturday		
Sunday		
Total Bankings		

BANK DIRECT CREDITS/DEBITS		
Credits:		
Total Credits:		
Debits:		
Interest		
Finance Charges		
Cashed Cheques		
Total Debits:		

WEEK'S BANK BALANCE		
£ at start of week		
+ Daily Bankings		
+ Direct Credits		
− Direct Debits		
− Chq. Payments		
Leaves: **Balance**		

BANK STATEMENT CHECK		
Statement Balance		
Add any bankings		
Less any cheques (Not yet on Statement)		
Leaves: **Balance**		

PAYMENTS RECORD

	Ref	BY CASH £	p	BY CHEQUE £	p
Stock/Raw Materials					
Stock/Raw Materials Sub-Totals					
Employee Costs — Staff Wages					
Staff PAYE/NIC					
Premises Costs — Business Rent					
Business Rates					
Cleaning					
Electric/Gas/Heat/Water					
Property Insurance					
Repairs — Repairs/Maintenance					
General Admin. Expenses — Business Insurances					
Postage/Parcels					
Stationery/Printing					
Subscriptions					
Sundries					
Telephone/Fax					
Motor Expenses — Fuel					
Repairs/Service					
Tax/Insurance					
Travel & Subsistence					
Advertising & Promotion					
Legal & Professional — Fees (eg Solicitor or Accountant)					
Other Expenses					
Drawings/NIC					
CAPITAL EXPENDITURE					
Total Cash & Cheque Payments					

Week 36

commencing . . . .

MONEY RECORD

Money in hand at start of week	£	p

DAILY TAKINGS

Monday		
Tuesday		
Wednesday		
Thursday		
Friday		
Saturday		
Sunday		
Total Takings		

OTHER MONEY, LOANS etc

Cash from Bank		
Total		

WEEK'S MONEY BALANCE

£ at start of week	
+ Daily Takings	
+ Other Money	
− Daily Bankings	
− Cash Payments	
Leaves: **Balance**	

Money in hand at end of week		

Discrepancy ±		

© P. Hingston

BANK RECORD

Bank Balance at start of week	£	p

DAILY BANKINGS

Monday		
Tuesday		
Wednesday		
Thursday		
Friday		
Saturday		
Sunday		
Total Bankings		

BANK DIRECT CREDITS/DEBITS

Credits:		
Total Credits:		
Debits:		
Interest		
Finance Charges		
Cashed Cheques		
Total Debits:		

WEEK'S BANK BALANCE

£ at start of week	
+ Daily Bankings	
+ Direct Credits	
− Direct Debits	
− Chq. Payments	
Leaves: **Balance**	

BANK STATEMENT CHECK

Statement Balance		
Add any bankings		
Less any cheques (Not yet on Statement)		
Leaves: **Balance**		

PAYMENTS RECORD

	Ref	BY CASH £	p	BY CHEQUE £	p
Stock/Raw Materials					
Stock/Raw Materials Sub-Totals					
Employee Costs — Staff Wages					
Staff PAYE/NIC					
Premises Costs — Business Rent					
Business Rates					
Cleaning					
Electric/Gas/Heat/Water					
Property Insurance					
Repairs — Repairs/Maintenance					
General Admin. Expenses — Business Insurances					
Postage/Parcels					
Stationery/Printing					
Subscriptions					
Sundries					
Telephone/Fax					
Motor Expenses — Fuel					
Repairs/Service					
Tax/Insurance					
Travel & Subsistence					
Advertising & Promotion					
Legal & Professional — Fees (eg Solicitor or Accountant)					
Other Expenses					
Drawings/NIC					
CAPITAL EXPENDITURE					
Total Cash & Cheque Payments					

Week **37**

commencing ....

MONEY RECORD

Money in hand at start of week	£	p

DAILY TAKINGS		
Monday		
Tuesday		
Wednesday		
Thursday		
Friday		
Saturday		
Sunday		
Total Takings		

OTHER MONEY, LOANS etc		
Cash from Bank		
Total		

WEEK'S MONEY BALANCE		
£ at start of week		
+ Daily Takings		
+ Other Money		
− Daily Bankings		
− Cash Payments		
Leaves: **Balance**		
Money in hand at end of week		
Discrepancy ±		

© P. Hingston

BANK RECORD

Bank Balance at start of week	£	p

DAILY BANKINGS		
Monday		
Tuesday		
Wednesday		
Thursday		
Friday		
Saturday		
Sunday		
Total Bankings		

BANK DIRECT CREDITS/DEBITS		
Credits:		
Total Credits:		
Debits:		
Interest		
Finance Charges		
Cashed Cheques		
Total Debits:		

WEEK'S BANK BALANCE		
£ at start of week		
+ Daily Bankings		
+ Direct Credits		
− Direct Debits		
− Chq. Payments		
Leaves: **Balance**		

BANK STATEMENT CHECK		
Statement Balance		
Add any bankings		
Less any cheques (Not yet on Statement)		
Leaves: **Balance**		

PAYMENTS RECORD

	Ref	BY CASH £	p	BY CHEQUE £	p
Stock/Raw Materials					
Stock/Raw Materials Sub-Totals					
Employee Costs — Staff Wages					
Staff PAYE/NIC					
Premises Costs — Business Rent					
Business Rates					
Cleaning					
Electric/Gas/Heat/Water					
Property Insurance					
Repairs — Repairs/Maintenance					
General Admin. Expenses — Business Insurances					
Postage/Parcels					
Stationery/Printing					
Subscriptions					
Sundries					
Telephone/Fax					
Motor Expenses — Fuel					
Repairs/Service					
Tax/Insurance					
Travel & Subsistence					
Advertising & Promotion					
Legal & Professional — Fees (eg Solicitor or Accountant)					
Other Expenses					
Drawings/NIC					
CAPITAL EXPENDITURE					
Total Cash & Cheque Payments					

Week **38**

commencing . . . .

MONEY RECORD

Money in hand at start of week	£	p

DAILY TAKINGS

Monday		
Tuesday		
Wednesday		
Thursday		
Friday		
Saturday		
Sunday		
Total Takings		

OTHER MONEY, LOANS etc

Cash from Bank		
Total		

WEEK'S MONEY BALANCE

£ at start of week		
+ Daily Takings		
+ Other Money		
− Daily Bankings		
− Cash Payments		
Leaves: **Balance**		

Money in hand at end of week		

Discrepancy ±		

© P. Hingston

BANK RECORD

Bank Balance at start of week	£	p

DAILY BANKINGS

Monday		
Tuesday		
Wednesday		
Thursday		
Friday		
Saturday		
Sunday		
Total Bankings		

BANK DIRECT CREDITS/DEBITS

Credits:		
Total Credits:		
Debits:		
Interest		
Finance Charges		
Cashed Cheques		
Total Debits:		

WEEK'S BANK BALANCE

£ at start of week		
+ Daily Bankings		
+ Direct Credits		
− Direct Debits		
− Chq. Payments		
Leaves: **Balance**		

BANK STATEMENT CHECK

Statement Balance		
Add any bankings		
Less any cheques (Not yet on Statement)		
Leaves: **Balance**		

PAYMENTS RECORD

	Ref	BY CASH £	p	BY CHEQUE £	p
Stock/Raw Materials					
Stock/Raw Materials Sub-Totals					
Employee Costs — Staff Wages					
Staff PAYE/NIC					
Premises Costs — Business Rent					
Business Rates					
Cleaning					
Electric/Gas/Heat/Water					
Property Insurance					
Repairs — Repairs/Maintenance					
General Admin. Expenses — Business Insurances					
Postage/Parcels					
Stationery/Printing					
Subscriptions					
Sundries					
Telephone/Fax					
Motor Expenses — Fuel					
Repairs/Service					
Tax/Insurance					
Travel & Subsistence					
Advertising & Promotion					
Legal & Professional — Fees (eg Solicitor or Accountant)					
Other Expenses					
Drawings/NIC					
CAPITAL EXPENDITURE					
Total Cash & Cheque Payments					

Week 39

commencing ....

MONEY RECORD

Money in hand at start of week	£	p

DAILY TAKINGS

	£	p
Monday		
Tuesday		
Wednesday		
Thursday		
Friday		
Saturday		
Sunday		
Total Takings		

OTHER MONEY, LOANS etc

Cash from Bank		
Total		

WEEK'S MONEY BALANCE

£ at start of week		
+ Daily Takings		
+ Other Money		
− Daily Bankings		
− Cash Payments		
Leaves: **Balance**		
Money in hand at end of week		
Discrepancy ±		

© P. Hingston

BANK RECORD

Bank Balance at start of week	£	p

DAILY BANKINGS

	£	p
Monday		
Tuesday		
Wednesday		
Thursday		
Friday		
Saturday		
Sunday		
Total Bankings		

BANK DIRECT CREDITS/DEBITS

Credits:		
Total Credits:		
Debits:		
Interest		
Finance Charges		
Cashed Cheques		
Total Debits:		

WEEK'S BANK BALANCE

£ at start of week		
+ Daily Bankings		
+ Direct Credits		
− Direct Debits		
− Chq. Payments		
Leaves: **Balance**		

BANK STATEMENT CHECK

	£	p
Statement Balance		
Add any bankings Less any cheques (Not yet on Statement)		
Leaves: **Balance**		

PAYMENTS RECORD

		Ref	BY CASH £	p	BY CHEQUE £	p
Stock/Raw Materials						
Stock/Raw Materials Sub-Totals						
Employee Costs	Staff Wages					
	Staff PAYE/NIC					
Premises Costs	Business Rent					
	Business Rates					
	Cleaning					
	Electric/Gas/Heat/Water					
	Property Insurance					
Repairs	Repairs/Maintenance					
General Admin. Expenses	Business Insurances					
	Postage/Parcels					
	Stationery/Printing					
	Subscriptions					
	Sundries					
	Telephone/Fax					
Motor Expenses	Fuel					
	Repairs/Service					
	Tax/Insurance					
Travel & Subsistence						
Advertising & Promotion						
Legal & Professional	Fees (eg Solicitor or Accountant)					
Other Expenses						
Drawings/NIC						
CAPITAL EXPENDITURE						
Total Cash & Cheque Payments						

Week 40

commencing ....

MONEY RECORD

Money in hand at start of week	£	p

DAILY TAKINGS

Monday		
Tuesday		
Wednesday		
Thursday		
Friday		
Saturday		
Sunday		
Total Takings		

OTHER MONEY, LOANS etc

Cash from Bank		
Total		

WEEK'S MONEY BALANCE

£ at start of week		
+ Daily Takings		
+ Other Money		
− Daily Bankings		
− Cash Payments		
Leaves: **Balance**		

Money in hand at end of week		

Discrepancy ±		

© P. Hingston

BANK RECORD

Bank Balance at start of week	£	p

DAILY BANKINGS

Monday		
Tuesday		
Wednesday		
Thursday		
Friday		
Saturday		
Sunday		
Total Bankings		

BANK DIRECT CREDITS/DEBITS

Credits:		
Total Credits:		
Debits:		
Interest		
Finance Charges		
Cashed Cheques		
Total Debits:		

WEEK'S BANK BALANCE

£ at start of week		
+ Daily Bankings		
+ Direct Credits		
− Direct Debits		
− Chq. Payments		
Leaves: **Balance**		

BANK STATEMENT CHECK

Statement Balance		
Add any bankings		
Less any cheques (Not yet on Statement)		
Leaves: **Balance**		

PAYMENTS RECORD

		Ref	BY CASH £	p	BY CHEQUE £	p
Stock/Raw Materials						
Stock/Raw Materials Sub-Totals						
Employee Costs	Staff Wages					
	Staff PAYE/NIC					
Premises Costs	Business Rent					
	Business Rates					
	Cleaning					
	Electric/Gas/Heat/Water					
	Property Insurance					
Repairs	Repairs/Maintenance					
General Admin. Expenses	Business Insurances					
	Postage/Parcels					
	Stationery/Printing					
	Subscriptions					
	Sundries					
	Telephone/Fax					
Motor Expenses	Fuel					
	Repairs/Service					
	Tax/Insurance					
Travel & Subsistence						
Advertising & Promotion						
Legal & Professional	Fees (eg Solicitor or Accountant)					
Other Expenses						
Drawings/NIC						
CAPITAL EXPENDITURE						
Total Cash & Cheque Payments						

Week 41

commencing............................

MONEY RECORD

Money in hand at start of week	£	p

DAILY TAKINGS
Monday		
Tuesday		
Wednesday		
Thursday		
Friday		
Saturday		
Sunday		
Total Takings		

OTHER MONEY, LOANS etc
Cash from Bank		
Total		

WEEK'S MONEY BALANCE
£ at start of week		
+ Daily Takings		
+ Other Money		
− Daily Bankings		
− Cash Payments		
Leaves: **Balance**		
Money in hand at end of week		
Discrepancy ±		

© P. Hingston

BANK RECORD

Bank Balance at start of week	£	p

DAILY BANKINGS
Monday		
Tuesday		
Wednesday		
Thursday		
Friday		
Saturday		
Sunday		
Total Bankings		

BANK DIRECT CREDITS/DEBITS
Credits:		
Total Credits:		
Debits:		
Interest		
Finance Charges		
Cashed Cheques		
Total Debits:		

WEEK'S BANK BALANCE
£ at start of week		
+ Daily Bankings		
+ Direct Credits		
− Direct Debits		
− Chq. Payments		
Leaves: **Balance**		

BANK STATEMENT CHECK
Statement Balance		
Add any bankings		
Less any cheques (Not yet on Statement)		
Leaves: **Balance**		

PAYMENTS RECORD

		Ref	BY CASH £	p	BY CHEQUE £	p
Stock/Raw Materials						
Stock/Raw Materials Sub-Totals						
Employee Costs	Staff Wages					
	Staff PAYE/NIC					
Premises Costs	Business Rent					
	Business Rates					
	Cleaning					
	Electric/Gas/Heat/Water					
	Property Insurance					
Repairs	Repairs/Maintenance					
General Admin. Expenses	Business Insurances					
	Postage/Parcels					
	Stationery/Printing					
	Subscriptions					
	Sundries					
	Telephone/Fax					
Motor Expenses	Fuel					
	Repairs/Service					
	Tax/Insurance					
Travel & Subsistence						
Advertising & Promotion						
Legal & Professional	Fees (eg Solicitor or Accountant)					
Other Expenses						
Drawings/NIC						
CAPITAL EXPENDITURE						
Total Cash & Cheque Payments						

Week **42**

commencing ....

MONEY RECORD

Money in hand at start of week	£	p

DAILY TAKINGS

Monday		
Tuesday		
Wednesday		
Thursday		
Friday		
Saturday		
Sunday		
Total Takings		

OTHER MONEY, LOANS etc

Cash from Bank		
Total		

WEEK'S MONEY BALANCE

£ at start of week		
+ Daily Takings		
+ Other Money		
− Daily Bankings		
− Cash Payments		
Leaves: **Balance**		

Money in hand at end of week		

Discrepancy ±		

© P. Hingston

BANK RECORD

Bank Balance at start of week	£	p

DAILY BANKINGS

Monday		
Tuesday		
Wednesday		
Thursday		
Friday		
Saturday		
Sunday		
Total Bankings		

BANK DIRECT CREDITS/DEBITS

Credits:		
Total Credits:		
Debits:		
Interest		
Finance Charges		
Cashed Cheques		
Total Debits:		

WEEK'S BANK BALANCE

£ at start of week		
+ Daily Bankings		
+ Direct Credits		
− Direct Debits		
− Chq. Payments		
Leaves: **Balance**		

BANK STATEMENT CHECK

Statement Balance		
Add any bankings		
Less any cheques (Not yet on Statement)		
Leaves: **Balance**		

PAYMENTS RECORD

		Ref	BY CASH £	p	BY CHEQUE £	p
Stock/Raw Materials						
Stock/Raw Materials Sub-Totals						
Employee Costs	Staff Wages					
	Staff PAYE/NIC					
Premises Costs	Business Rent					
	Business Rates					
	Cleaning					
	Electric/Gas/Heat/Water					
	Property Insurance					
Repairs	Repairs/Maintenance					
General Admin. Expenses	Business Insurances					
	Postage/Parcels					
	Stationery/Printing					
	Subscriptions					
	Sundries					
	Telephone/Fax					
Motor Expenses	Fuel					
	Repairs/Service					
	Tax/Insurance					
Travel & Subsistence						
Advertising & Promotion						
Legal & Professional	Fees (eg Solicitor or Accountant)					
Other Expenses						
Drawings/NIC						
CAPITAL EXPENDITURE						
Total Cash & Cheque Payments						

Week 43

commencing ....

MONEY RECORD

Money in hand at start of week	£	p

DAILY TAKINGS		
Monday		
Tuesday		
Wednesday		
Thursday		
Friday		
Saturday		
Sunday		
Total Takings		

OTHER MONEY, LOANS etc		
Cash from Bank		
Total		

WEEK'S MONEY BALANCE		
£ at start of week		
+ Daily Takings		
+ Other Money		
− Daily Bankings		
− Cash Payments		
Leaves: Balance		
Money in hand at end of week		
Discrepancy ±		

© P. Hingston

BANK RECORD

Bank Balance at start of week	£	p

DAILY BANKINGS		
Monday		
Tuesday		
Wednesday		
Thursday		
Friday		
Saturday		
Sunday		
Total Bankings		

BANK DIRECT CREDITS/DEBITS		
Credits:		
Total Credits:		
Debits:		
Interest		
Finance Charges		
Cashed Cheques		
Total Debits:		

WEEK'S BANK BALANCE		
£ at start of week		
+ Daily Bankings		
+ Direct Credits		
− Direct Debits		
− Chq. Payments		
Leaves: Balance		

BANK STATEMENT CHECK		
Statement Balance		
Add any bankings		
Less any cheques (Not yet on Statement)		
Leaves: Balance		

PAYMENTS RECORD

	Ref	BY CASH £	p	BY CHEQUE £	p
Stock/Raw Materials					
Stock/Raw Materials Sub-Totals					
Employee Costs — Staff Wages					
Employee Costs —					
Employee Costs —					
Employee Costs — Staff PAYE/NIC					
Premises Costs — Business Rent					
Premises Costs — Business Rates					
Premises Costs — Cleaning					
Premises Costs — Electric/Gas/Heat/Water					
Premises Costs — Property Insurance					
Repairs — Repairs/Maintenance					
General Admin. Expenses — Business Insurances					
General Admin. Expenses — Postage/Parcels					
General Admin. Expenses — Stationery/Printing					
General Admin. Expenses — Subscriptions					
General Admin. Expenses — Sundries					
General Admin. Expenses — Telephone/Fax					
Motor Expenses — Fuel					
Motor Expenses — Repairs/Service					
Motor Expenses — Tax/Insurance					
Travel & Subsistence					
Advertising & Promotion					
Legal & Professional — Fees (eg Solicitor or Accountant)					
Other Expenses					
Drawings/NIC					
CAPITAL EXPENDITURE					
Total Cash & Cheque Payments					

Week 44

commencing . . . .

MONEY RECORD

Money in hand at start of week	£	p

DAILY TAKINGS		
Monday		
Tuesday		
Wednesday		
Thursday		
Friday		
Saturday		
Sunday		
Total Takings		

OTHER MONEY, LOANS etc		
Cash from Bank		
Total		

WEEK'S MONEY BALANCE		
£ at start of week		
+ Daily Takings		
+ Other Money		
− Daily Bankings		
− Cash Payments		
Leaves: Balance		

Money in hand at end of week		

Discrepancy ±		

© P. Hingston

BANK RECORD

Bank Balance at start of week	£	p

DAILY BANKINGS		
Monday		
Tuesday		
Wednesday		
Thursday		
Friday		
Saturday		
Sunday		
Total Bankings		

BANK DIRECT CREDITS/DEBITS		
Credits:		
Total Credits:		
Debits:		
Interest		
Finance Charges		
Cashed Cheques		
Total Debits:		

WEEK'S BANK BALANCE		
£ at start of week		
+ Daily Bankings		
+ Direct Credits		
− Direct Debits		
− Chq. Payments		
Leaves: Balance		

BANK STATEMENT CHECK		
Statement Balance		
Add any bankings		
Less any cheques (Not yet on Statement)		
Leaves: Balance		

PAYMENTS RECORD

	Ref	BY CASH £	p	BY CHEQUE £	p
Stock/Raw Materials					
Stock/Raw Materials Sub-Totals					
Employee Costs — Staff Wages					
Staff PAYE/NIC					
Premises Costs — Business Rent					
Business Rates					
Cleaning					
Electric/Gas/Heat/Water					
Property Insurance					
Repairs — Repairs/Maintenance					
General Admin. Expenses — Business Insurances					
Postage/Parcels					
Stationery/Printing					
Subscriptions					
Sundries					
Telephone/Fax					
Motor Expenses — Fuel					
Repairs/Service					
Tax/Insurance					
Travel & Subsistence					
Advertising & Promotion					
Legal & Professional — Fees (eg Solicitor or Accountant)					
Other Expenses					
Drawings/NIC					
CAPITAL EXPENDITURE					
Total Cash & Cheque Payments					

Week 45

commencing ....

MONEY RECORD

Money in hand at start of week	£	p

DAILY TAKINGS		
Monday		
Tuesday		
Wednesday		
Thursday		
Friday		
Saturday		
Sunday		
Total Takings		

OTHER MONEY, LOANS etc		
Cash from Bank		
Total		

WEEK'S MONEY BALANCE		
£ at start of week		
+ Daily Takings		
+ Other Money		
− Daily Bankings		
− Cash Payments		
Leaves: Balance		

Money in hand at end of week		
Discrepancy ±		

© P. Hingston

BANK RECORD

Bank Balance at start of week	£	p

DAILY BANKINGS		
Monday		
Tuesday		
Wednesday		
Thursday		
Friday		
Saturday		
Sunday		
Total Bankings		

BANK DIRECT CREDITS/DEBITS		
Credits:		
Total Credits:		
Debits:		
Interest		
Finance Charges		
Cashed Cheques		
Total Debits:		

WEEK'S BANK BALANCE		
£ at start of week		
+ Daily Bankings		
+ Direct Credits		
− Direct Debits		
− Chq. Payments		
Leaves: Balance		

BANK STATEMENT CHECK		
Statement Balance		
Add any bankings Less any cheques (Not yet on Statement)		
Leaves: Balance		

PAYMENTS RECORD

	Ref	BY CASH £	p	BY CHEQUE £	p
Stock/Raw Materials					
Stock/Raw Materials Sub-Totals					
Employee Costs — Staff Wages					
Staff PAYE/NIC					
Premises Costs — Business Rent					
Business Rates					
Cleaning					
Electric/Gas/Heat/Water					
Property Insurance					
Repairs — Repairs/Maintenance					
General Admin. Expenses — Business Insurances					
Postage/Parcels					
Stationery/Printing					
Subscriptions					
Sundries					
Telephone/Fax					
Motor Expenses — Fuel					
Repairs/Service					
Tax/Insurance					
Travel & Subsistence					
Advertising & Promotion					
Legal & Professional — Fees (eg Solicitor or Accountant)					
Other Expenses					
Drawings/NIC					
CAPITAL EXPENDITURE					
Total Cash & Cheque Payments					

Week 46

commencing . . . .

MONEY RECORD

Money in hand at start of week	£	p

DAILY TAKINGS		
Monday		
Tuesday		
Wednesday		
Thursday		
Friday		
Saturday		
Sunday		
Total Takings		

OTHER MONEY, LOANS etc		
Cash from Bank		
Total		

WEEK'S MONEY BALANCE		
£ at start of week		
+ Daily Takings		
+ Other Money		
− Daily Bankings		
− Cash Payments		
Leaves: Balance		

Money in hand at end of week		

Discrepancy ±		

© P. Hingston

BANK RECORD

Bank Balance at start of week	£	p

DAILY BANKINGS		
Monday		
Tuesday		
Wednesday		
Thursday		
Friday		
Saturday		
Sunday		
Total Bankings		

BANK DIRECT CREDITS/DEBITS		
Credits:		
Total Credits:		
Debits:		
Interest		
Finance Charges		
Cashed Cheques		
Total Debits:		

WEEK'S BANK BALANCE		
£ at start of week		
+ Daily Bankings		
+ Direct Credits		
− Direct Debits		
− Chq. Payments		
Leaves: Balance		

BANK STATEMENT CHECK		
Statement Balance		
Add any bankings		
Less any cheques (Not yet on Statement)		
Leaves: Balance		

PAYMENTS RECORD

	Ref	BY CASH £	p	BY CHEQUE £	p
Stock/Raw Materials					
Stock/Raw Materials Sub-Totals					
Employee Costs — Staff Wages					
Employee Costs — Staff PAYE/NIC					
Premises Costs — Business Rent					
Premises Costs — Business Rates					
Premises Costs — Cleaning					
Premises Costs — Electric/Gas/Heat/Water					
Premises Costs — Property Insurance					
Repairs — Repairs/Maintenance					
General Admin. Expenses — Business Insurances					
General Admin. Expenses — Postage/Parcels					
General Admin. Expenses — Stationery/Printing					
General Admin. Expenses — Subscriptions					
General Admin. Expenses — Sundries					
General Admin. Expenses — Telephone/Fax					
Motor Expenses — Fuel					
Motor Expenses — Repairs/Service					
Motor Expenses — Tax/Insurance					
Travel & Subsistence					
Advertising & Promotion					
Legal & Professional — Fees (eg Solicitor or Accountant)					
Other Expenses					
Drawings/NIC					
CAPITAL EXPENDITURE					
Total Cash & Cheque Payments					

Week 47

commencing . . . .

PAYMENTS RECORD

	Ref	BY CASH £	p	BY CHEQUE £	p
Stock/Raw Materials					
Stock/Raw Materials Sub-Totals					
Employee Costs — Staff Wages					
Staff PAYE/NIC					
Premises Costs — Business Rent					
Business Rates					
Cleaning					
Electric/Gas/Heat/Water					
Property Insurance					
Repairs — Repairs/Maintenance					
General Admin. Expenses — Business Insurances					
Postage/Parcels					
Stationery/Printing					
Subscriptions					
Sundries					
Telephone/Fax					
Motor Expenses — Fuel					
Repairs/Service					
Tax/Insurance					
Travel & Subsistence					
Advertising & Promotion					
Legal & Professional — Fees (eg Solicitor or Accountant)					
Other Expenses					
Drawings/NIC					
CAPITAL EXPENDITURE					
Total Cash & Cheque Payments					

MONEY RECORD

	£	p
Money in hand at start of week		

DAILY TAKINGS

Monday		
Tuesday		
Wednesday		
Thursday		
Friday		
Saturday		
Sunday		
Total Takings		

OTHER MONEY, LOANS etc

Cash from Bank		
Total		

WEEK'S MONEY BALANCE

£ at start of week		
+ Daily Takings		
+ Other Money		
− Daily Bankings		
− Cash Payments		
Leaves: **Balance**		
Money in hand at end of week		
Discrepancy ±		

© P. Hingston

BANK RECORD

	£	p
Bank Balance at start of week		

DAILY BANKINGS

Monday		
Tuesday		
Wednesday		
Thursday		
Friday		
Saturday		
Sunday		
Total Bankings		

BANK DIRECT CREDITS/DEBITS

Credits:		
Total Credits:		
Debits:		
Interest		
Finance Charges		
Cashed Cheques		
Total Debits:		

WEEK'S BANK BALANCE

£ at start of week		
+ Daily Bankings		
+ Direct Credits		
− Direct Debits		
− Chq. Payments		
Leaves: **Balance**		

BANK STATEMENT CHECK

Statement Balance		
Add any bankings		
Less any cheques (Not yet on Statement)		
Leaves: **Balance**		

Week **48**

commencing . . . .

PAYMENTS RECORD

	Ref	BY CASH £	p	BY CHEQUE £	p
Stock/Raw Materials					
Stock/Raw Materials Sub-Totals					

MONEY RECORD

Money in hand at start of week	£	p

DAILY TAKINGS

Monday		
Tuesday		
Wednesday		
Thursday		
Friday		
Saturday		
Sunday		
Total Takings		

OTHER MONEY, LOANS etc

Cash from Bank		
Total		

WEEK'S MONEY BALANCE

£ at start of week		
+ Daily Takings		
+ Other Money		
− Daily Bankings		
− Cash Payments		
Leaves: **Balance**		

Money in hand at end of week		
Discrepancy ±		

© P. Hingston

BANK RECORD

Bank Balance at start of week	£	p

DAILY BANKINGS

Monday		
Tuesday		
Wednesday		
Thursday		
Friday		
Saturday		
Sunday		
Total Bankings		

BANK DIRECT CREDITS/DEBITS

Credits:		
Total Credits:		
Debits:		
Interest		
Finance Charges		
Cashed Cheques		
Total Debits:		

WEEK'S BANK BALANCE

£ at start of week		
+ Daily Bankings		
+ Direct Credits		
− Direct Debits		
− Chq. Payments		
Leaves: **Balance**		

BANK STATEMENT CHECK

Statement Balance		
Add any bankings Less any cheques (Not yet on Statement)		
Leaves: **Balance**		

PAYMENTS RECORD (continued)

		Ref	BY CASH £	p	BY CHEQUE £	p
Employee Costs	Staff Wages					
	Staff PAYE/NIC					
Premises Costs	Business Rent					
	Business Rates					
	Cleaning					
	Electric/Gas/Heat/Water					
	Property Insurance					
Repairs	Repairs/Maintenance					
General Admin. Expenses	Business Insurances					
	Postage/Parcels					
	Stationery/Printing					
	Subscriptions					
	Sundries					
	Telephone/Fax					
Motor Expenses	Fuel					
	Repairs/Service					
	Tax/Insurance					
Travel & Subsistence						
Advertising & Promotion						
Legal & Professional	Fees (eg Solicitor or Accountant)					
Other Expenses						
Drawings/NIC						
CAPITAL EXPENDITURE						
Total Cash & Cheque Payments						

Week 49

commencing........................

MONEY RECORD

Money in hand at start of week	£	p

DAILY TAKINGS		
Monday		
Tuesday		
Wednesday		
Thursday		
Friday		
Saturday		
Sunday		
Total Takings		

OTHER MONEY, LOANS etc		
Cash from Bank		
Total		

WEEK'S MONEY BALANCE		
£ at start of week		
+ Daily Takings		
+ Other Money		
− Daily Bankings		
− Cash Payments		
Leaves: Balance		

Money in hand at end of week		
Discrepancy ±		

© P. Hingston

BANK RECORD

Bank Balance at start of week	£	p

DAILY BANKINGS		
Monday		
Tuesday		
Wednesday		
Thursday		
Friday		
Saturday		
Sunday		
Total Bankings		

BANK DIRECT CREDITS/DEBITS		
Credits:		
Total Credits:		
Debits:		
Interest		
Finance Charges		
Cashed Cheques		
Total Debits:		

WEEK'S BANK BALANCE		
£ at start of week		
+ Daily Bankings		
+ Direct Credits		
− Direct Debits		
− Chq. Payments		
Leaves: Balance		

BANK STATEMENT CHECK		
Statement Balance		
Add any bankings		
Less any cheques (Not yet on Statement)		
Leaves: Balance		

PAYMENTS RECORD

	Ref	BY CASH £	p	BY CHEQUE £	p
Stock/Raw Materials					
Stock/Raw Materials Sub-Totals					
Employee Costs — Staff Wages					
Employee Costs —					
Employee Costs —					
Employee Costs — Staff PAYE/NIC					
Premises Costs — Business Rent					
Premises Costs — Business Rates					
Premises Costs — Cleaning					
Premises Costs — Electric/Gas/Heat/Water					
Premises Costs — Property Insurance					
Repairs — Repairs/Maintenance					
General Admin. Expenses — Business Insurances					
General Admin. Expenses — Postage/Parcels					
General Admin. Expenses — Stationery/Printing					
General Admin. Expenses — Subscriptions					
General Admin. Expenses — Sundries					
General Admin. Expenses — Telephone/Fax					
Motor Expenses — Fuel					
Motor Expenses — Repairs/Service					
Motor Expenses — Tax/Insurance					
Travel & Subsistence					
Advertising & Promotion					
Legal & Professional — Fees (eg Solicitor or Accountant)					
Other Expenses					
Drawings/NIC					
CAPITAL EXPENDITURE					
Total Cash & Cheque Payments					

Week **50**

commencing.............................

MONEY RECORD

Money in hand at start of week	£	p

DAILY TAKINGS
Monday		
Tuesday		
Wednesday		
Thursday		
Friday		
Saturday		
Sunday		
Total Takings		

OTHER MONEY, LOANS etc
Cash from Bank		
Total		

WEEK'S MONEY BALANCE
£ at start of week		
+ Daily Takings		
+ Other Money		
− Daily Bankings		
− Cash Payments		
Leaves: **Balance**		

Money in hand at end of week		

Discrepancy ±		

© P. Hingston

BANK RECORD

Bank Balance at start of week	£	p

DAILY BANKINGS
Monday		
Tuesday		
Wednesday		
Thursday		
Friday		
Saturday		
Sunday		
Total Bankings		

BANK DIRECT CREDITS/DEBITS
Credits:		
Total Credits:		
Debits:		
Interest		
Finance Charges		
Cashed Cheques		
Total Debits:		

WEEK'S BANK BALANCE
£ at start of week		
+ Daily Bankings		
+ Direct Credits		
− Direct Debits		
− Chq. Payments		
Leaves: **Balance**		

BANK STATEMENT CHECK
Statement Balance		
Add any bankings		
Less any cheques (Not yet on Statement)		
Leaves: **Balance**		

PAYMENTS RECORD

	Ref	BY CASH £	p	BY CHEQUE £	p
Stock/Raw Materials					
Stock/Raw Materials Sub-Totals					
Employee Costs — Staff Wages					
Staff PAYE/NIC					
Premises Costs — Business Rent					
Business Rates					
Cleaning					
Electric/Gas/Heat/Water					
Property Insurance					
Repairs — Repairs/Maintenance					
General Admin. Expenses — Business Insurances					
Postage/Parcels					
Stationery/Printing					
Subscriptions					
Sundries					
Telephone/Fax					
Motor Expenses — Fuel					
Repairs/Service					
Tax/Insurance					
Travel & Subsistence					
Advertising & Promotion					
Legal & Professional — Fees (eg Solicitor or Accountant)					
Other Expenses					
Drawings/NIC					
CAPITAL EXPENDITURE					
Total Cash & Cheque Payments					

Week 51

commencing.........................

MONEY RECORD

	£	p
Money in hand at start of week		

DAILY TAKINGS

	£	p
Monday		
Tuesday		
Wednesday		
Thursday		
Friday		
Saturday		
Sunday		
Total Takings		

OTHER MONEY, LOANS etc

Cash from Bank		
Total		

WEEK'S MONEY BALANCE

£ at start of week		
+ Daily Takings		
+ Other Money		
− Daily Bankings		
− Cash Payments		
Leaves: Balance		
Money in hand at end of week		

Discrepancy ±		

© P. Hingston

BANK RECORD

	£	p
Bank Balance at start of week		

DAILY BANKINGS

Monday		
Tuesday		
Wednesday		
Thursday		
Friday		
Saturday		
Sunday		
Total Bankings		

BANK DIRECT CREDITS/DEBITS

Credits:		
Total Credits:		
Debits:		
Interest		
Finance Charges		
Cashed Cheques		
Total Debits:		

WEEK'S BANK BALANCE

£ at start of week		
+ Daily Bankings		
+ Direct Credits		
− Direct Debits		
− Chq. Payments		
Leaves: Balance		

BANK STATEMENT CHECK

Statement Balance		
Add any bankings		
Less any cheques (Not yet on Statement)		
Leaves: Balance		

PAYMENTS RECORD

	Ref	BY CASH £	p	BY CHEQUE £	p
Stock/Raw Materials					
Stock/Raw Materials Sub-Totals					
Employee Costs — Staff Wages					
Staff PAYE/NIC					
Premises Costs — Business Rent					
Business Rates					
Cleaning					
Electric/Gas/Heat/Water					
Property Insurance					
Repairs — Repairs/Maintenance					
General Admin. Expenses — Business Insurances					
Postage/Parcels					
Stationery/Printing					
Subscriptions					
Sundries					
Telephone/Fax					
Motor Expenses — Fuel					
Repairs/Service					
Tax/Insurance					
Travel & Subsistence					
Advertising & Promotion					
Legal & Professional — Fees (eg Solicitor or Accountant)					
Other Expenses					
Drawings/NIC					
CAPITAL EXPENDITURE					
Total Cash & Cheque Payments					

Week 52

commencing..............................

MONEY RECORD

Money in hand at start of week	£	p

DAILY TAKINGS

Monday		
Tuesday		
Wednesday		
Thursday		
Friday		
Saturday		
Sunday		
Total Takings		

OTHER MONEY, LOANS etc

Cash from Bank		
Total		

WEEK'S MONEY BALANCE

£ at start of week		
+ Daily Takings		
+ Other Money		
− Daily Bankings		
− Cash Payments		
Leaves: Balance		

Money in hand at end of week		

Discrepancy ±		

© P. Hingston

BANK RECORD

Bank Balance at start of week	£	p

DAILY BANKINGS

Monday		
Tuesday		
Wednesday		
Thursday		
Friday		
Saturday		
Sunday		
Total Bankings		

BANK DIRECT CREDITS/DEBITS

Credits:		
Total Credits:		
Debits:		
Interest		
Finance Charges		
Cashed Cheques		
Total Debits:		

WEEK'S BANK BALANCE

£ at start of week		
+ Daily Bankings		
+ Direct Credits		
− Direct Debits		
− Chq. Payments		
Leaves: Balance		

BANK STATEMENT CHECK

Statement Balance		
Add any bankings		
Less any cheques (Not yet on Statement)		
Leaves: Balance		

PAYMENTS RECORD

		Ref	BY CASH £	p	BY CHEQUE £	p
Stock/Raw Materials						
Stock/Raw Materials Sub-Totals						
Employee Costs	Staff Wages					
	Staff PAYE/NIC					
Premises Costs	Business Rent					
	Business Rates					
	Cleaning					
	Electric/Gas/Heat/Water					
	Property Insurance					
Repairs	Repairs/Maintenance					
General Admin. Expenses	Business Insurances					
	Postage/Parcels					
	Stationery/Printing					
	Subscriptions					
	Sundries					
	Telephone/Fax					
Motor Expenses	Fuel					
	Repairs/Service					
	Tax/Insurance					
Travel & Subsistence						
Advertising & Promotion						
Legal & Professional	Fees (eg Solicitor or Accountant)					
Other Expenses						
Drawings/NIC						
CAPITAL EXPENDITURE						
Total Cash & Cheque Payments						

Week **53**

commencing ....

MONEY RECORD

Money in hand at start of week	£	p

DAILY TAKINGS		
Monday		
Tuesday		
Wednesday		
Thursday		
Friday		
Saturday		
Sunday		
Total Takings		

OTHER MONEY, LOANS etc		
Cash from Bank		
Total		

WEEK'S MONEY BALANCE		
£ at start of week		
+ Daily Takings		
+ Other Money		
− Daily Bankings		
− Cash Payments		
Leaves: **Balance**		

Money in hand at end of week		

Discrepancy ±		

© P. Hingston

BANK RECORD

Bank Balance at start of week	£	p

DAILY BANKINGS		
Monday		
Tuesday		
Wednesday		
Thursday		
Friday		
Saturday		
Sunday		
Total Bankings		

BANK DIRECT CREDITS/DEBITS		
Credits:		
Total Credits:		
Debits:		
Interest		
Finance Charges		
Cashed Cheques		
Total Debits:		

WEEK'S BANK BALANCE		
£ at start of week		
+ Daily Bankings		
+ Direct Credits		
− Direct Debits		
− Chq. Payments		
Leaves: **Balance**		

BANK STATEMENT CHECK		
Statement Balance		
Add any bankings Less any cheques (Not yet on Statement)		
Leaves: **Balance**		

PAYMENTS RECORD

		Ref	BY CASH £	p	BY CHEQUE £	p
Stock/Raw Materials						
Stock/Raw Materials Sub-Totals						
Employee Costs	Staff Wages					
	Staff PAYE/NIC					
Premises Costs	Business Rent					
	Business Rates					
	Cleaning					
	Electric/Gas/Heat/Water					
	Property Insurance					
Repairs	Repairs/Maintenance					
General Admin. Expenses	Business Insurances					
	Postage/Parcels					
	Stationery/Printing					
	Subscriptions					
	Sundries					
	Telephone/Fax					
Motor Expenses	Fuel					
	Repairs/Service					
	Tax/Insurance					
Travel & Subsistence						
Advertising & Promotion						
Legal & Professional	Fees (eg Solicitor or Accountant)					
Other Expenses						
Drawings/NIC						
CAPITAL EXPENDITURE						
Total Cash & Cheque Payments						

At Year End
1st task: Stock Taking

Instructions On the last day of your tax year, if you hold stock or raw material, you should do a stock-take. The form below should help. You multiply the Qty (quantity) of each item by its "unit price". The unit price is normally its cost price including VAT (as you are not VAT-reg'd), or its selling price if lower. List only stock that is saleable. Continue on a separate sheet, if needed. Note you should also do stock-takes during the year to ensure you hold adequate but not excessive stock.

© P. Hingston

Stock/Raw Material Description	Qty	Unit Price £	p	Value £	p
Total					

Stock/Raw Material Description	Qty	Unit Price £	p	Value £	p
Total					

At Year End
Next tasks . . .

Instructions If you are buying or selling on credit, you need to list below all your Debtors and Creditors. Include goods or services bought/sold in the year even if not yet invoiced. If necessary, continue the list on a separate sheet.

Instructions (following pages) The next three pages summarise the 52 (or 53) Weekly pages. Opposite is a summary of the MONEY and BANK RECORD columns. Then follows two pages which summarise the PAYMENTS RECORD columns.

YEAR END LIST OF DEBTORS (people who owe you money)

Debtor's Name	Details (eg Invoice No)	Total £	p
Total			

YEAR END LIST OF CREDITORS (people you owe money to)

Creditor's Name	Details (eg Invoice No)	Total (inc VAT) £	p
Total			

© P. Hingston

CAPITAL EXPENDITURE (& SALES OF ASSETS)

Description of Assets BOUGHT During Year	Date Purchased	Cost (inc VAT) £	p

Instructions Capital expenditure covers the purchase of fixed assets such as vehicles, machinery, tools, office equipment etc. For taxation purposes these are treated differently to revenue expenditure (such as stock purchases, wages, rent etc) so should be listed separately here. The list should relate to the CAPITAL EXPENDITURE payments you recorded on your Weekly pages. Finally, since the sale of an asset can have tax implications, that should be listed too.

Description of Assets SOLD During Year	Date Sold	Price £	p

ANNUAL SUMMARY of MONEY RECORD   ANNUAL SUMMARY of BANK RECORD

© P. Hingston

Wk No	Weekly Total Takings		Other Money, Loans etc						Weekly Total Bankings		Bank Direct Credits/Debits							Interest		Finance Charges		Cashed Cheques	
			Cash from Bank																				
1																							
2																							
3																							
4																							
5																							
6																							
7																							
8																							
9																							
10																							
11																							
12																							
13																							
14																							
15																							
16																							
17																							
18																							
19																							
20																							
21																							
22																							
23																							
24																							
25																							
26																							
27																							
28																							
29																							
30																							
31																							
32																							
33																							
34																							
35																							
36																							
37																							
38																							
39																							
40																							
41																							
42																							
43																							
44																							
45																							
46																							
47																							
48																							
49																							
50																							
51																							
52																							
53																							
Total																							

ANNUAL SUMMARY of PAYMENTS RECORD (Note: For each entry add the Cash and Cheque payments together)

© P. Hingston

| Wk No | Stock/ Raw Material | | Employee Costs | | Drawings & NIC | | Premises Costs | | | | | | | | | Repairs | | General Admin. Expenses | | | | | | Wk No |
							Rent/Rates		Cleaning		Utilities		Insurance					Insurances		Post/Parcels		Stat./Print		
1																									1
2																									2
3																									3
4																									4
5																									5
6																									6
7																									7
8																									8
9																									9
10																									10
11																									11
12																									12
13																									13
14																									14
15																									15
16																									16
17																									17
18																									18
19																									19
20																									20
21																									21
22																									22
23																									23
24																									24
25																									25
26																									26
27																									27
28																									28
29																									29
30																									30
31																									31
32																									32
33																									33
34																									34
35																									35
36																									36
37																									37
38																									38
39																									39
40																									40
41																									41
42																									42
43																									43
44																									44
45																									45
46																									46
47																									47
48																									48
49																									49
50																									50
51																									51
52																									52
53																									53
Total																									

	General Admin. Expenses (cont'd)			Motor Expenses	Travel & Subsistence	Advertising & Promotion	Legal & Professional	Other Expenses			Capital Expenditure	WEEKLY TOTALS	Wk No
	Subscriptions	Sundries	Tel/Fax										
1													1
2													2
3													3
4													4
5													5
6													6
7													7
8													8
9													9
10													10
11													11
12													12
13													13
14													14
15													15
16													16
17													17
18													18
19													19
20													20
21													21
22													22
23													23
24													24
25													25
26													26
27													27
28													28
29													29
30													30
31													31
32													32
33													33
34													34
35													35
36													36
37													37
38													38
39													39
40													40
41													41
42													42
43													43
44													44
45													45
46													46
47													47
48													48
49													49
50													50
51													51
52													52
53													53
tal													

Cashflow Forecast

What Is Its Purpose?

If you have never done a Cashflow Forecast before then you may be forgiven for thinking it is just something else to waste your valuable time and only relevant to "big business", but this is not so. One of the most common reasons a business gets into financial trouble is due to "cashflow problems". This usually occurs when goods (or services) are bought on credit and later when the bills come in there is no money (or overdraft facility) to meet those bills. Cashflow problems may result from the business being under-capitalised, having poor sales or suffering from bad payers. This can also affect an otherwise profitable business.

In every business, cash comes in . . . . . but so do the bills and it can soon become difficult to control. This is where a Cashflow Forecast is useful as it helps you to forecast your future cash requirements and any problems can be spotted early and something done about it.

How Does It Work?

A Cashflow Forecast is just that – a forecast of the cash (ie all the money) flowing in and out of the business for the year ahead. At this stage you may be saying "that's impossible", but it can be done with sufficient accuracy to make the effort worthwhile. And it will take a bit of effort to complete, particularly if your business is new and some of your figures are little better than good guesses.

Most businesses (new or established) will find the CASH OUT figures are straightforward to estimate. But a new business will find line 1 difficult to predict. In that case you could do a "break-even" cashflow where you complete the form leaving line 1 to the very end and then you insert what sales you need to at least keep the bottom line 33 positive or within your overdraft limit.

Below, lines 6 to 29 reflect the same headings (in alphabetical order) as the weekly BANK and PAYMENTS RECORDs.

Worked Example

The worked example (below right) shows the first 12 weeks trading of a small shop which has just opened. The vertical columns can be in months or 4-week periods, whichever you prefer (but since this Accounts Book is weekly, you may find the 4-week periods easier).

In this example, to start the business the proprietor is providing £6500 capital, there is a bank loan of £2000, and there is an overdraft facility of at least £1750. (Note: The figures at the foot of the cashflow are in brackets indicating the bank account is in overdraft).

© P. Hingston

	CASH IN								
1	Takings (ie Sales)								1
2	Bank or other Loans								2
3	Owner's Capital								3
4	Other Money In								4
5	TOTAL CASH IN								5
	CASH OUT								
6	Advertising & Promotion								6
7	Business Rent								7
8	Business Rates								8
9	Cleaning								9
10	Drawings/NIC								10
11	Electric/Gas/Heat/Water								11
12	Finance Charges								12
13	Insurances								13
14	Interest								14
15	Legal & Professional								15
16	Motor – Fuel								16
17	– Repairs/Service								17
18	– Tax/Insurance								18
19	Other Expenses								19
20	Postage/Parcels								20
21	Repairs & Maintenance								21
22	Staff Wages & PAYE/NIC								22
23	Stationery/Printing								23
24	Stock/Raw Materials								24
25	Subscriptions								25
26	Sundries								26
27	Telephone/Fax								27
28	Travel & Subsistence								28
29	CAPITAL EXPENDITURE								29
30	TOTAL CASH OUT								30
31	Net Cashflow								31
32	Opening Balance								32
33	CLOSING BALANCE								33

In the example, as the business is new, the "Opening Balance" on line 32 is zero. Also, stock purchases exceed sales in the initial weeks as the shop is stocking-up. As the weeks roll on, stock purchases on line 24 should relate to sales on line 1 (if not, the business is carrying either too little or too much stock).

Doing Your Own Cashflow Forecast

Two points before you start . . . (1) as any prediction becomes more hazy as you look further into the future, you may try forecasting only 2-3 months ahead at a time if you prefer; (2) a golden rule with Cashflow Forecasts is to be pessimistic and in particular to not underestimate overheads or overestimate likely sales.

Method

1. Decide whether you will work in months or 4-week periods and enter them across the top (note: Column 13 will only be needed if you are working in 4-week periods).

2. Omit £ signs and exclude pence.

3. Work in pencil, since (a) you will probably need to make several attempts to complete the form and (b) when you have completed the first 4 weeks trading you can rub out that column's pencil figures and insert the actual figures in ink. You can then see *actual* from *forecast*.

4. The *actual* figures come from your Weekly pages, so for instance, line 1 is found by adding together the "Total Takings" of the appropriate weeks. Likewise, line 6 is found by adding up all the "Advertising & Promotion" payments (cash and cheque) for the same weeks.

5. If you are offering credit, as this is a forecast of *cash* flow, then you show the "Sales" in the 4-week (or month) column when you expect to receive the money.

6. Now do line 1 for the whole form

(unless you are doing a "break-even" cashflow in which case this is done last).

7. Complete lines 2 to 4 for the *first* vertical column and total up on line 5.

8. When you've completed lines 6 to 29 for the first column, total up on line 30 to get the total cash out during that period.

9. Next subtract line 30 from line 5 to get the "Net Cashflow" on line 31.

10. Finally add lines 31 and 32 to get the "Closing Balance" for that first column.

11. This "Closing Balance" becomes the "Opening Balance" for the next column.

12. Repeat steps 7 to 11 for column two.

Finally, never confuse cash *inflow* with *profitability*. And remember the bottom line of a Cashflow Forecast does not represent either a "profit" or a "loss".

Column 13

				TOTALS
1				
2				
3				
4				
5				
6				
7				
8				
9				
10				
11				
12				
13				
14				
15				
16				
17				
18				
19				
20				
21				
22				
23				
24				
25				
26				
27				
28				
29				
30				
31				
32				
33				

WORKED EXAMPLE © P. Hingston

	CASH IN	Weeks 1-4	Weeks 5-8	Wks 9-12
1	Takings (ie Sales)	1000	1500	2000
2	Bank or other Loans		2000	
3	Owner's Capital	6500		
4	Other Money In			
5	TOTAL CASH IN	7500	3500	2000
	CASH OUT			
6	Advertising & Promotion	200		
7	Business Rent	1000	250	250
8	Business Rates			
9	Cleaning			
10	Drawings/NIC		300	300
11	Electric/Gas/Heat/Water		75	
12	Finance Charges		80	80
13	Insurances	350		
14	Interest			44
15	Legal & Professional	300		
16	Motor – Fuel			
17	– Repairs/Service			
18	– Tax/Insurance			
19	Other Expenses			
20	Postage/Parcels			
21	Repairs & Maintenance		50	
22	Staff Wages & PAYE/NIC			
23	Stationery/Printing	20		
24	Stock/Raw Materials	5000	3000	1500
25	Subscriptions			
26	Sundries	80	50	30
27	Telephone/Fax	250	50	
28	Travel & Subsistence			
29	CAPITAL EXPENDITURE	1450		
30	TOTAL CASH OUT	8650	3855	2204
31	Net Cashflow	(1150)	(355)	(204)
32	Opening Balance	0	(1150)	(1505)
33	**CLOSING BALANCE**	(1150)	(1505)	(1709)

VITAL DATES

On this page you can note important dates, such as: **Insurances** (eg the renewal dates for all insurances); **Vehicle** (eg the dates when the Tax disc expires, the "MoT" is needed or servicing is due); **Financial** (eg when Rent/Rates are due or tax is to be paid); **Staff** (eg dates when staff join or leave, are off sick or on holiday).

© P. Hingston

JANUARY	FEBRUARY	MARCH	APRIL

MAY	JUNE	JULY	AUGUST

SEPTEMBER	OCTOBER	NOVEMBER	DECEMBER

Acknowledgements The author gratefully acknowledges the assistance of Stuart Ramsden FCA. And special thanks to Charlotte Hingston for the cover design and help generally with this book. Also many thanks to Sue Holmes and those users who made useful suggestions.

Note In the worked examples given in this book all characters and businesses are fictitious.

Important Although we have tried to ensure the accuracy of information in this book, no responsibility for loss occasioned to any person acting or refraining from action as a result of material in this book can be accepted by the author or publisher. Due to the complexities involved in accounting and taxation, we strongly advise the reader to take professional advice.

Suggestions Although the author welcomes constructive comments or suggestions, he is not able to handle queries relating to readers' personal business matters. These queries are best referred to a Local Enterprise Agency, T.E.C., L.E.C., business development unit, professional adviser or relevant government department.